A Farmer's Boy

By the same author:
A Farmer's Lot . . .

'Ideal bedside book. It will send you off to sleep chuckling.'
The Sunday Post.

'An inexpensive tonic for the long winter nights.'
The Scotsman.

A Farmer's Boy

Fordyce Maxwell

Illustrated by Graham Lang

Bridge Studios
Northumberland
1989

First published in Great Britain in 1989

by Bridge Studios,
   Kirklands,
   The Old Vicarage,
   Scremerston,
   Berwick upon Tweed,
   Northumberland.
   TD15 2RB

   Tel. 0289 302658/330274

ISBN 1 872010 05 9

Typeset by EMS Phototypesetting, Berwick upon Tweed.
Printed by Martin's of Berwick.

For my father

Arrival

The rat looked at me. I looked at the rat. It began to uncurl from where it lay on my side of the bed. For a second we both froze.

I had seen rats before at the old farm. But I had seen them from a distance as they shot into holes with their snake-like wiggling run, close to the ground with the long tail whipping behind.

This time we were nose to nose. I could see, clearly, the brown hair beginning to stiffen, the scaly tail starting to twitch, the whiskers, the teeth and the eyes.

The hate I saw there was, no doubt, imaginary. But when you're six, tired, in strange, half-lit surroundings and on the point of climbing into bed with a rat, imagination is a powerful force.

It had been a long day. I stood in bare feet on bare boards, in danger of running splinters into the soles, in pyjamas, ready to climb into bed. That was when I pulled back the sheet and blanket and we looked closely at each other.

There only seemed one thing to do. I did it. I leapt back and yelled. The rat was almost as quick. It sprang from the fold-down couch bed and bolted across the floor.

Dad spun round from the gas mantle he was fiddling with.

'What is it?'

I couldn't speak, but pointed to where the rat was fighting its way behind a box in the corner of the room. The last of the tail disappeared as Dad squinted into the shadows.

'A mouse?' he asked, going back to the gas mantle.

I shook my head and stuttered: 'R . . r . . rat!'

He spun round.

'What? Damnation,' he shouted and ran to the door. He yanked it open, while keeping a wary eye on the corner where the rat had gone. He shouted again into the darkness: 'Fan! Fan! Here, lass.'

1

The collie had settled down for the night in what passed for a kitchen. She was reluctant to move. There was no patter of paws on stone as we waited.

'Fan!'

A note in his voice encouraged her. There were faint sounds of movement from the darkness beyond, and a scraffling noise from the rat in the corner.

The note in his voice became imperative as the rat showed every sign of leaving the corner and heading for the door he was holding ajar. That must have been the way it came in during the afternoon when it had the house to itself, a liberty it, and probably family, friends and relations had enjoyed for some time.

Fan quickened her pace through the stone-floored, dank and empty room between our makeshift bedroom and the kitchen. She slipped through the door with teeth bared as

2

Arrival

the rat decided it was now or never.

Dog and rat became aware of each other. Dad became aware of the fact that he had made two tactical mistakes – one, to be in bare feet and shirt tail, the other to be directly between Fan and the rat. All three seemed to pause for one deep breath.

The old farmhouse front-room where we had pitched our fold-down couch was the only habitable part of the building. The fire, lighted earlier for cheerfulness as much as warmth, threw shadows on the walls. The gas mantle was hissing steadily, casting its own shadows, shadows which became frantically animated as dog and rat met, too close to the man's bare feet and exposed legs for comfort.

Dad jigged energetically clear of the snapping teeth, swinging powerfully and indiscriminately with the coal shovel. The dog with a rat at bay was single-minded. He knew her teeth were as dangerous as the rat's and took no chances. I did my bit by yelling steadily while torn between jumping onto the couch to avoid the free-for-all, or staying where I was on the grounds that where one large brown rat had come from there might well be more.

This agony of indecision didn't last much longer. Fan got in a glancing nip on the rat which squealed, spun and bit her nose. It hung on savagely while she yowled with pain and tried to shake it free. They thrashed among Dad's feet despite his superhuman efforts to stay airborne and defy the law of gravity.

I had made my decision at first squeal and now had a clear view of proceedings from the couch. Dad leapt higher and swung the shovel faster. A series of ringing blows finally dislodged the rat, knocking it upside down and sideways.

Fan, who had received a fair proportion of the blows to her head, paused only to shake her ears and look at him with a pained expression.

Tired from the long day, previously drowsy from the fire and bedtime cocoa, but now on the brink of hysteria, I watched. There was a final, momentary, stillness of shadows. They they were off in the flickering firelight on a macabre steeplechase over the sparse furniture.

Over, through or under, depending on size and inclination, they went, taking in the wooden-armed chair with the sagging seat, the small upright wooden chair, a small table, a chest of drawers, a packing case and a few cardboard boxes. And the couch, which they took like fox-hunters.

It wasn't clear, and Dad could never decide himself, whether he was in the lead or bringing up the rear. He felt that as long as he was clear of the rat he didn't much care. But the pace was too hot to last. Furniture crashed to the accompaniment of yelps and squeals. Dad saved his breath for sprinting, but I made up for him, yelling more with excitement than fright as Fan finally got the rat.

Once bitten only made her more certain when she got a

second chance. The rat squealed as she bit hard and tossed it into the air. There was silence except for the dull thud as Dad made absolutely sure with the shovel, slid the deceased onto it, opened the window and threw it as far as he could into the overgrown garden.

I hugged the collie with relief. He gave her a brief pat on the head before sending her back to the kitchen. Then we inspected the couch closely from several angles before deciding it was safe to climb in.

He had to get out again to turn off the gas, poking up the embers of the fire while he was there. Lying rigid under the blanket, still thinking of the rat, I could see his profile in the glow – the high forehead where the black hair was already receding, the eagle-nose, the powerful jaw.

I compared them with my own, half-formed, and taking entirely after my mother.

He put the poker down and stood for a minute or two looking out thoughtfully through the small-paned window, across the valley into Berwickshire. A few lights still shone across the Tweed. He sighed and came to bed.

First Day

I woke early next morning and wondered, briefly, where I was. Dad was already on his way out.

'Lie still,' he said. 'Go back to sleep. I'll make some breakfast when I get in.'

I raised my head cautiously and looked round. Now I was wide awake.

'No more rats?' I asked.

'No more rats,' he said, closing the door behind him.

I pulled the blanket up to eye-level. Now I remembered where I was. Only a day ago we had been climbing into the green van to leave home for ever.

The worry about that was overcome by the discomfort. We carried a variety of tools and equipment, furniture, a suitcase and the collie. We clanked as we drove and Fan sat uneasily on the shifting load.

We drove up the Avenue to the A1 and turned right to head further north. The police car stopped us between Belford and Fenwick. The policeman looked with interest at the way the van sat down on its springs.

'Out early this morning, sir. Your van? Driver's licence? Did you know your near-side brake light isn't working?'

'There's nothing wrong with it,' Dad said to me as the policeman continued to prowl round. 'Little enough to do, that's their problem.'

'Just one more thing – sir. Does the handbrake work? Only you seem to have parked without it, relying on the gear box. Not recommended.'

'Work?' Dad said. 'Of course it works.'

'In that case would you like to try it?'

'Try it?'

'Yes – sir. Pull your handbrake on – if you don't mind.'

Dad slipped into the driver's seat and yanked the hand

brake. There was a slight creak, but it jammed on firmly. The policeman looked at it closely. He seemed satisfied.

'Good morning, then. Sorry to trouble you – but get that brake light fixed.'

'Right. I will.'

The police car pulled away. We sat still. Gradually it disappeared up the long straight towards Berwick.

'Are we going?'

'Yes. Just a minute.'

Eventually he moved, not to start the van but to get a crowbar which was among the clanking heap in the back.

'It went on all right,' he muttered, as he began to lever the handbrake up far enough to release the spring catch. 'But I knew it wouldn't come off.'

He looked over his shoulder: 'Keep your eye open for that police car coming back.'

It didn't. With the handbrake finally released we set off again. Left at Fenwick, over the moor to Ford, round the Blue Bell corner, right at the garage at Cornhill towards Berwick. And there it was.

It sat on the hill. We turned off the main road onto a pot-holed one made of stones and railway ballast. Grass grew up the centre. It was almost half a mile from the overgrown wood at the road end to the steading, with three gates to open and shut on the way.

The van, heavily loaded, found it hard going.

The first stretch was level, with a deceptively sharp right hand corner leading to the hump-backed bridge over the railway line. Several fresh splashes of cement shone white between the stones.

'That's to see if the bridge is cracking,' Dad said. 'There's a lot of heavy traffic about now. But not a lot up here.'

We went over the hump-back cautiously. The first gate lay lop-sided on one hinge. Dad had to get out and open it, drive through, then get out again and shut it.

We drove round a bend onto the first hill. At the top was the second gate, which I managed to open and close. There were watering holes on either side, sunk into the ground on the long-grass verge. Thick green weed was thriving, but the water looked clean.

'That's the emergency water supply,' Dad said. He wasn't joking.

This gate was followed by a level ground S-bend.

'That was to give the horses a rest,' Dad said. What I couldn't understand was why they built farms on hills in the first place.

The second rise levelled out briefly, after the S-bend, beside a sycamore tree with an oddly-flat top then rose again. This was the shortest, but steepest stretch.

Loose ballast skittered below the tyres as we drove level with a stone wall, standing in places, surrounding a derelict orchard with a few scrubby apple trees.

The third gate at the top was also closed. I managed to jump out and open it before a chubby lad, about my age, could get through the cottage garden gate. He stepped back and glared through rails as we turned the corner with the cottage on the left, the bothy, byre and farmhouse on the right.

We parked beside the row of three pigsties. There were slates missing, old muck in the pens and rat droppings in several places. We could see part of the house through the narrow gap between byre and calf pens.

Dad stretched, clasping his hands behind the back of his head in a characteristic gesture.

'We're looking at the good bits.'

He went round to the back of the van to let the collie out and handed me a chair.

'Here – make youself useful.'

We walked through the gap into a small yard. Straight ahead was the kitchen and back door, on our right the main length of the single-storey house. In time I would sort out the irregular rectangle of buildings, each one joined to the next with an assortment of slate, tile and corrugated iron roofs. But now we went into the house, making several trips with our belongings.

It was cold and damp. Old, dull, brown and green paints were the main colour scheme. Where wallpaper was peeling it was possible to see many thin layers. There was a built-in tub and boiler in the corner of the kitchen, and one cold water tap. There were two rooms at the front with wooden floors, big open fireplaces, low doorways and small windows in thick walls. It was in the slightly better of the two that we made our bed and met the rat.

'It's not a very nice house,' I said, shivering slightly.

'It soon will be,' he replied, with his usual optimism. 'Come on, let's see if everything else is still standing.'

We walked into the yard, where the cattle yard joined directly on to the washhouse, and opened a door. A dusty passage went past usable, but worm-eaten, wooden calf pens. This had once been the stable, with a double-door at the far end. He opened one of them.

We looked out on a hotchpotch of low roofed, corrugated iron sheds; a longer shed made of old sleepers, with an asbestos roof; and a wall which ran along the top of the yard.

'They're not very good are they?'

'No they're not,' he said shortly. 'But they're all we've got at the minute.'

We walked up the yard to the wall, turned left and found ourselves back at the pigsties.

'Well, that's the grand tour. Let's walk the fields.'

We went through the gateway at the House Field. A small, rectangular brick structure rose out of the ground. That was the water supply, pumped up from the windmill two fields away. The pipes produced a trickle which people made rude remarks about, and compared to their own ability.

'We'll have to do something about that,' he said. 'We need a decent water supply for the house and we'll be carrying a lot more stock.'

We passed the end of the cottage going into the House Field. The boy had come onto the back green from a wooden lean-to shed. We looked closely at each other, but didn't speak.

'That's John,' Dad said. 'His father's the tractorman here. We'll get our dinner with him until the house's ready for your mum and the kids.'

He pulled a rough map from his pocket.

'Right – Three Corner Field at the railway bridge. Sugar beet – not that you'd know it. We'll look at the road end fields later. The Quarry Field is half way to Berwick for some reason.'

We walked up the House Field, my short legs struggling with the uneven ground. He checked on the map as we walked.

'Tatties. Rape. Fallow. Hard to say which is which. I thought it might have improved since I last saw it. I think it's got worse.'

At the top of the rise he shaded his eyes and looked round.

'That's a fine view.'

We could see the Eildons, the Cheviots, Duns Law, almost to the coast. Closer at hand we could see farms in the valley bottom and along the sides of the smaller hills. Or sitting on top of a hill, like us.

'Pity it doesn't pay the rent.'

'Look,' I said, from where I had been grubbing in the soil, having tired of the view. 'I've found a tattie.'

'Sure it's not a marble?' He inspected it and kicked it into the distance.

'Goal!'

We stumbled across fallow land. It had a healthy crop of weeds which compared favourably with most of the other crops we found.

'The next one's the Pond End. Then the Windmill Field.'

The windmill, really a wind pump, stood in one corner. It looked like a small pylon, with a vaned, circular sail which spun when the wind blew, driving the wooden connecting rod which drove the pump. This field had oats in it.

'Near Bog – three acres oats, six acres barley. Far Bog – grass. Little Baldrons – about seven acres turnips. Big Baldrons – nine acres oats.'

These four fields were the flattest on the farm. None had been cut. All were thin and weedy. They didn't shimmer under the early morning September sun, or wave in the breeze.

We turned back towards the steading. Melkington big house and steading were now on the hill to our right. Sun glinted on the windows.

'Our Fox Cover – six acres, grass. Hayshed Field – grass.'

The hayshed itself was wooden, with a red tile roof falling in on some old, black hay. It stood alone, on a rise, opposite the depression which gave the Pond End its name. It was more mudhole than pond, and smelt.

Opposite the scrub orchard was the Little Whirly Field, spring barley on a steep slope. The House Croft, beyond the overgrown garden, was the boundary fence with Hotel

Lands farm. At the bottom, the lonnen crossed the farm road and led, eventually, to the village.

Standing in the orchard we turned to look at the house and what we could see of the buildings. This included a filled in, ornately arched window and a stone dovecote. I picked up a windfall apple, green, but sharply sweet, and bit into it. An apple flavour is hard to describe, but impossible to forget. It was the taste of a new beginning for me, each autumn, as long as that tree stood.

'Well,' he said, 'do you think it's worth £2.12 shillings and six pence an acre rent?'

I chewed thoughtfully on the apple. The bare house, poor buildings and weeds loomed in my mind. I was struggling with tables at school and knew there were twelve pennies in a shilling. An acre was an unknown quantity.

'It seems a lot of money.'

He ruffled my hair.

'It does. It seems a lot to me too.'

Early Days

Jake drove the red David Brown tractor which pulled the binder. Dad sat on this, behind the windmill-type wooden blades, above the chattering knife and rolling canvas. In a good crop he would have been happy as sheaves whistled off the slide onto the ground as fast as the knotter could tie the strings.

In the Nine Acre Bog we travelled the length of one side to garner a sheaf. I trotted beside the binder, bare legs scratched and scraped by the stubble, delighted to be out of school into the September sunshine.

As the tractor chugged, and the binder clacked and clattered, they were moving in towards the centre of the field. In a good crop this was the time the rabbits began to make a run for it, while dogs and men with sticks tried to stop them.

Not in the Nine Acre Bog. There was hardly enough

straw to hide a fieldmouse, never mind a rabbit. Fan nosed about hopefully, but not a rabbit broke cover.

Pulling a clump of stubble up by the roots, with soil attached, made a useful missile. Thrown into the air, the soil-heavy roots brought it down like, I fondly thought, a hand grenade. Fan yelped as I bounced one off her back, a lucky strike.

The tractor and binder stopped for a short tea break. Jake produced a haversack which held a flask of black tea, and a worn tin with thick cheese sandwiches. He sat down on the stubble with his back against the tractor wheel. When he'd finished he lit a pipe with a metal top, tamping down the tobacco and puffing contentedly. The smoke rose almost straight in the stillness.

Dad perched on the edge of the binder with his cup of tea

and scone, then got up and walked about, checking the binder, looking at the tractor wheels, inspecting a sheaf, studying what was still to cut.

'Not a good crop,' he said. I looked up from inspecting my scratched legs, wondering when a scone might head my way. Fan was looking at him with the same thought. It was either telepathy, or the fact that we were both drooling, because he passed over the last scone. I shared it with the dog and wished for more.

'No, not the best crop I've ever seen. What was it like last year, Jake?'

Jake took his pipe out and paused before answering.

'About the same I'd say. He wasn't a great man for fertiliser.'

All the spring barley crops, in the fertiliser-starved fields were poor. The crop of Onward oats in the Windmill Field was little better.

'You can say that again,' Dad grunted, flicking out the dregs of his tea. 'I'd say these fields'll run about five hundredweights an acre.'

'Is that very bad?'

'About as bad as I expected. At least the weather's good. School all right?'

'Fine.'

I didn't like to tell him how long the day was, how long the walk up the tree-lined lonnen, how frightened I was of the black dog at the level crossing. I was having trouble learning my tables and was petrified of the headmaster. Apart from that, school was fine and I liked my teacher, Mrs Whittle.

I knew he had enough problems of his own.

It wasn't the farm everyone would have chosen, In fact it wasn't the farm anyone would have chosen who felt they still had much choice. After a series of disappointments, he didn't feel that he had.

He thought, when he saw the advert, that no one would be as desperate or determined to get a farm as he was. After inspecting the fields, the steading, and the house as an afterthought, he was positive.

A family had grown old in it over 50 years. They were replaced by the unlucky, fast-moving, previous tenant, short of money and experience. He struggled on for six years then moved by moonlight. The crops he left were thin and poor. Buildings and house were simply poor.

Estate and solicitor weren't geared to moving quickly. Advertising for an immediate tenant unsettled them. Dad, and valuer Harry Hunter, walked the 153 neglected acres, talked it over in the car, drove back to the solicitors and made an offer. It was a decisive move which took the estate, and my mother, by surprise.

Within ten days he was tenant in name. A week after that two of us moved in with the rats, legendary locally for size and population.

After years of free-running, they didn't surrender territory easily to dog or poison. They fought back by crawling, weak with poison, under the front room floorboards to die. There, in the rat equivalent of an elephant' graveyard, they died and decayed until floorboards were ripped up in a frenzy to remove the corpses.

In those first few weeks they were on the lengthy list of worries, but not near the top. There was a harvest to bring in, thin and weedy though it was.

For most farmers it had been a good year. Yields were above average for most crops. The stormy August was followed by an Indian-summer September. Potato yields were a record and root crops were excellent. All of which was completely irrelevant to us.

The dealer was another problem. When we arrived, he had cattle grazing in the far-flung quarry Field. He made his position plain when he drove up to the steading.

'I paid a rent for that field. Fair rent as well. You're a reasonable man. You'll let the cattle stay to the end of October?'

He was a beefy man, inclined to shout.

'Sorry. But you didn't pay any rent to me,' Dad said. 'I need the field. They'll have to go.'

'Go? Where? I've got my grazing all worked out. Where am I going to shift them for two months?'

Braces held his trousers at half-mast over a bulging gut. He wore yellow-tan boots and carried a stick.

'That's not my problem,' Dad answered. 'I've enough worries of my own. Just get them moved.'

The dealer dug his stick vicously into the ballast at his feet.

'There'll be trouble. I paid a rent for that field.'

They glared at each other. Dad kept his voice down below a shout.

'I you don't get them moved I'll turn them onto the main road and head them in your direction.'

The dealer, redder and beefier with each exchange, waved his stick.

'Right! Right! I'll move them. But you haven't heard the last of it. I hope anything you put in that field drops dead.'

He struggled back into his car, his short legs kicking violently as he jammed his gut behind the steering wheel. He shot into reverse, spun round and hurtled towards the corner. That was when he realised that John, anxious as ever to help, had shut the gate again. In a flurry of ballast, he slid sideways to end up an inch or two from the gate post. He leapt out, gut and jowls wobbling with fury, to find that the gate opened towards his car.

I watched, fascinated. I'd never seen a human being explode before. I was ready to see fragments of braces, dinner and yellow-tan boots spread over the road. Tyres spun and ballast flew as he forced himself behind the wheel once more and reversed. He jumped out, ran to the gate and smashed it round. It bounced off the verge and caught him a nasty crack on the ankle. That was when he screamed and shook his fist. I'd never seen anyone shake a fist either, except in The Dandy.

'I hope they all die,' he bawled, purple in the face.

'What – all of them?' Dad said innocently.

'Baaah!'

He drove off in a cloud, as Jake said, who had been

16

watching with interest from his front door, of shit, fur and feathers. We waited for the squeal of brakes as he came to the next gate. And the last one. Then I was sent down to make sure they were closed.

'A dealer's curse,' Dad said. 'Just what we need.'

The Quarry Field was divided by the actual quarry, which had provided stone for the bridges during the railway building of the 1860s. It was our furthest-flung field.

On any sensible basis, it should have been part of Melkington. In return, we should have had the Melkington field which came right up to one side of our farm road. But some long-forgotten deal had exchanged them, leaving us with the Quarry Field – stiff clay patches, boulder-covered hill face, water filled quarry and all.

It was in grass of a sort. When the dealer, with final bad grace, had sent a lorry for the cattle, we put Half Bred ewes

into the field. A few weeks later we introduced the Suffolk
tup to them.

We took him along in the green van. He was reluctant to
get in, but once there stood calmly, looking over Dad's
shoulder as we trundled along the road.

There was an explosion of wind from the back of the van,
followed by a series of smaller ones. The window on Dad's
side was jammed. I wound my side down as fast as I could
as he gagged a little, then opened his door in desperation.

We both looked at the tup. The deep brown eyes in a
black face looked mildly back at us. He exploded again as
we rocketed into the gateway and I threw myself out to
open it. Dad accelerated through, ignoring the ruts,
slammed the brakes on and flung open the back doors.
There was a final blast as we tried to turn him round, and
he tried to climb into the front seat.

Once out, Dad took him by surprise by catching a back leg and shoulder and throwing him into a sitting position.

'Pass me the keel.'

He rubbed the thick, oily marking fluid onto the tup's breastbone with a bit of stick. The tup showed what he thought of this by exploding again.

'What's that red stuff for?'

The tup, on his feet by now, set off at a stately pace to inspect the ewes. They began to appear from various parts of the field to inspect him. He began to sniff closely at one which took his fancy.

'It's to show which ewes he's tupped.' He added thoughtfully, to himself, as the tup mounted his first ewe: 'It's a good job they don't keel humans. There'd be a few worried characters round here.'

The mating seemed to be satisfactory. I felt I was learning all the time. As we drove away, the ewe had a clear, tell-tale red keel mark on her rump and the tup was already getting friendly with another

'Happy as larry,' Dad said as we left. 'I hope he can pace himself.'

Next morning there were eight red-rumped ewes. But no tup.

'Probably resting,' Dad said. 'We'd better find him all the same.'

He walked round the big side of the field. I took the small side. We walked right round the quarry before looking in it.

One end fell away gradually. That was the end the council were starting to use as a rubbish dump. The other end was a sheer drop of twenty feet into water. Our exploding friend was floating peacefully there.

Dad passed his hand over his eyes and rubbed his chin. He threw a stone into the water close to the carcase. Ripples spread, but there was no sign of life. We turned and walked away.

Later in the morning, with the aid of a crook, the tup was hauled through the water towards the shallows, Dad lay on his stomach and fastened a rope round the tup's chest. As he forced a knot into place his wristwatch snagged on the wool. He made a grab too late. He lay quietly and watched it slide away into the green depths.

The other end of the rope was fastened to the David Brown and the carcase hauled, unceremoniously, up the bramble-covered banking. The tup was buried and a replacement bought for £11. It, and the ewes, ran on the Pond End to avoid any repeat of the dealer's curse. It was the last time he wore a wristwatch.

He didn't need one. If it was daylight, he was working. As days got shorter, nights longer and darker, he was working anyway. My mother told him, when she got the chance at weekends, that some of it was self-inflicted. He was trying to do everything at once.

Livestock was the main work load in the tumble-down,

unlighted buildings where every job took twice as long as it should have done. Despite my mother, and the advice of my Uncle Sam, he was determined to get as much livestock on the farm as he could afford, as soon as possible.

Sam's advice was to concentrate on cropping until the final settlement of the partnership, with my Uncle John, was sorted out. It was a system which would mean a smaller overdraft and less work until he found his feet.

The stubborn streak in the whole family hadn't missed him. We had a house-cow, pigs, hens, sheep and cattle. Time passed in a blur.

Finally, there was the house to occupy his mind. Plans for it went wrong. The best one, which would have been to knock the lot down and start again, wasn't acceptable. Plan B was for the two of us to rough it until it was fit for a family to live in.

That was always going to take time. Materials were scarce. Planning permission was needed. The estate was again caught cold. Their agents were in London – they raised difficulties about what they would pay for and, worse, did it slowly.

He dealt, and was allowed to deal, only with intermediaries. Our landlord in those early days was a remote figure. That explained our open surprise when one autumn day a dark-suited, stooped, figure with a pale face and slightly bloodshot eyes, stepped into the yard.

He carried his hat in one hand and a walking stick in the other. Dad, impressed by this obvious effort to see how the new tenant was managing, and hopeful that perhaps a visit by the landlord in person would get things moving, went to meet him.

The old man looked at him coolly.

'Mrs Maxwell in?' he asked.

'No,' Dad said, 'we . . .'

'Hmmph,' said the old captain, turned his back and walked out of my life.

Dad flushed.

'Rude old . . .', he said, then remembered I was there.

'I'll be glad when his son takes over.'

The disappointed landlord's visit did nothing to speed up change, as we moved into another year.

Jean

'What do you think, Tammy?'

We were in the small farm steading at the end of the village. Dad looked hopefully over a disintegrating stone wall at a group of cattle and I looked at his questioner.

The brown face under an elderly cap was lined and leathery, with brown eyes in a web of wrinkles. A clay pipe was stuck in one corner of the mouth, puffing out small gouts of smoke, and the other corner turned up with a half smile. It was a face like a friendly crabapple.

An old sports jacket hung loose on narrow shoulders. Baggy trousers flapped at the ankles of heavy brown boots. The clothes hung and fitted where they touched on a worn body, with a bowed back and rough, small hands.

Her name was Jean. She was the tenant of Hotel Lands farm and one of our immediate neighbours. At one time she had run a small dairy from these cramped yards and buildings. Her sister, a sturdy, strapping woman usually in wellingtons and sacking apron, unhindered by a cleft palate, looked after these cattle.

They were Red Polls, thickset, shortlegged, one of the dual-purpose breeds which produced beef calves as well as rich milk. In summer she would walk them through the village to their grazing field beside the railway station. In winter they stayed in the byre and yards. She sold the milk round the village from a pony and trap.

I didn't remember that. Now the dairy cattle had gone and Jean was struggling. She had a large household which included herself, two sisters, two former prisoners of war, two Irish setters and a colony of cats.

She was kind-hearted and a soft touch, and there were hard-bitten farmers and dealers who had no qualms about

taking advantage of that. Cattle and sheep grazed her fields
for which she never got full payment. They palmed poor
quality stock off on her, cancelling efforts made by more
generous neighbours to help her along.

Above all, she was aye ahint. Crops were late to go in,
late to be harvested, weedy and unthrifty. She had a
tractor, a thing of joy to Adolph, one of the regulars, but she
believed horses would make a comeback.

Days were spent raking the countryside to farm sales,
buying up horse harnesses and brasses, when she should
have been working or at least making sure that the rest
were. She also bought a large collection of other rubbish
which was going to come in handy some day. We were
standing beside heaps of it as we looked over the wall.

She repeated the question, which Dad didn't seem to
have heard. His hopes had flickered and died while he
looked over the wall. There was a selection of rough, Irish-
bred cattle wolfing down poor hay.

'Where did you get them Jean?'

'Kerrigan the dealer. He owed for a few months' grazing.
All they need's a bit of feeding and get the horns off.'

'Get the horns off them, eh?'

He looked again at the varied bunch.

'They've got horns like coat racks. Have you any idea
how you'll get them off?'

'Well, there's me and Adolph – and I thought you'd
maybe lend a bit hand, Tammy?'

He'd been waiting for that, so he wasn't disappointed.
The last time we'd given Jean 'a bit hand' it had taken a
day to haul home the remnants of a threshing machine from
a farm sale. Adolph had tried to pull it with their own
David Brown and, in the attempt, a wheel had fallen off.
Chasing cattle and catching cockerels, lending machinery,
running repairs – he'd done them all. He sighed.

'Getting horns like that off is a vet's job.'

'All right, Can you give him a ring for me?'

The pipe went back in and the eyes smiled, as she
removed her cap and rubbed the close-cropped grey hair. It

was an irresistible request. Dad looked over the wall again. A gaunt, bony, blue-grey with horns like a stag and a back like the roof of a house looked morosely back.

'Well, I don't know. I'm busy enough myself . . .'

'Come and have a cup of tea and have a think about it.'

'Ah . . .'

There was no way out. What he liked about cats could be written on the end of a matchbox. It didn't include the distinctive cat aroma of the five-room cottage, which mingled richly with that of dogs, cooking, log fire and people who worked outdoors and lived indoors in much the same clothes.

'Visitors, Lil.'

Lil, the housekeeping sister, was already setting the table for tea. Adolph and the other worker sat stolidly in a corner, waiting. Cats were moving in various directions, rattled by the unexpected activity. The setters, glossy and boisterous, bounded round the room.

I sat where I was told to sit wide eyed. Dad sat on a wooden chair at the table, opposite Jean, and started to drink a cup of tea. A cat climbed onto the table and walked across it in a leisurely way. Dad's cup stopped half way to his mouth as Jean gently lifted the cat down.

'These beese, Tammy.'

He was still gazing at where the cat had been. One of the setters appeared under the table and started to nuzzle between his legs. He pushed it away.

'Er . . . what? Sorry, Jean?'

The setter liked this game. It came back and nuzzled again. He pushed it away more forcefully. Jean was drinking tea and looking at the fire.

'These beese, then. We'll get the horns off them soon, eh?'

The setter came back a third time. He clamped his formidable right hand on its muzzle, like a rat-trap, continuing to drink tea with his left. The dog didn't like that so much. Claws scrabbled frantically on the oilcloth as it tried to back away.

Jean looked under the table.

'Is that dog all right, Tammy?'

She couldn't see the hand tighten a little more on the dog's nose. It gave a muffled howl.

'It's fine, Jean."

The muffled yowl sounded like a dog trying to throw its voice.

'Are you sure?'

Dad let go and the setter accelerated backwards, crashing off Jean's chair. It stood in the corner shaking its head and squinting down its nose for several minutes.

'Funny. I've never seen it act like that.'

Adolph and the other worker were advancing on the tea table and Mame, the third sister, had come in. Cats were rëurning from various directions and Jean threw another log on the fire. There was a fullness about that room which seemed to impress Dad.

'We'll have to be going,' he said briskly, standing up. As

he made for the door with me close behind, he stopped to look at a certificate on the wall. It was for a ploughing championship. Jean smiled and nodded.

'That's a few years ago now, Tammy. The East Learmouth championship. More than 20 competitors. Horse ploughing of course.'

'When did you start working with horses?'

'Back during the war. The First war, like. Just a lassie.'

She threw her head back and laughed, the brown, leathery face splitting to show teeth browned by forty years of pipe smoking.

'Just a lassie, Tammy. Driving a pair of horse and doing a man's job. And I've been deeing it ever since.'

There was a short silence. Next door there was a steady clink and clatter of knives and crockery, but no conversation.

'Right, then, We'll get a day to do them cattle. Cheerio.'

He remained doubtful about the long-term prospects for Jean's cattle. So did the vet, as we prepared to move among them a few days later.

Getting them into the wooden, worm-eaten, cattle crush was not easy. Adolph was brave, and impervious to pain, but leaden-footed. Jean was quicker on her feet, but slightly built. The second worker had wisely chosen to be absent. After one perilous close-up of a bullock's steaming nostrils, I was swung up into a hay-heck out of the way.

It left Dad and the vet to do most of the harrying and chasing, with occasional two-word bursts in German from Adolph, in his outfit of faded blue shirt, faded blue overalls and tackity boots.

After several near misses, with steam rising on the autumn morning air, a bullock finally crashed into the crush. The back door slammed behind it, but it took some time to get the horns through the gap at the front to allow the sliding yoke to jam its neck.

It was Dad who managed to manoeuvre the horns through, without being gutted like a trout as the bullock swung its head. Once the head was through it did its best to turn turtle and throttle itself, while he kept his thick fingers clamped on the nostrils. Jean was pushing firmly, but mainly ineffectually, from the back and getting trod on.

The vet was trying feverishly to close what looked like giant bolt cutters over one massive horn. With a final grunt he succeeded. It severed with a crunch and fell, slowly, like a small tree, blood fountaining outwards and upwards. The vet skipped to one side and most of it missed him. But not all. Cursing, he dived straight at the other horn as if about to bite it off rather than cut it.

Briefly, there were three heads locked together. The vet, bent double and clenching teeth and muscles. Dad, clutching the bullock's nose and grinding his teeth together with effort. The blue-grey bullock, threshing and jumping stiff-legged. All three were hidden from view, at intervals, by a fresh mist of blood while Jean, from the back, and Adolph, from a safe distance, encouraged their efforts.

It was a basic, brutal, tableau. All human, and a lot of animal, life was there. Old Gilroy appeared round the corner and put his head over the wall.

'Aye,' he said, 'grand morning.'

The second horn creaked and crumpled to the ground as he gave his opinion. The vet looked up, sweat streaming down his blood-spattered face, as Dad reached for the catch at the front of the stocks to let the bullock out, while trying to avoid the continuing spray of blood.

'What?'

'Er . . . grand morning?'

As the old man spoke, the bullock burst out of the stocks, careered across the yard to join the rest, and tried to climb the wall. Adolph swore volubly, and the old man disappeared the way he had come.

Dad, the vet, and Jean looked at each other. They looked at the blood-stained faces, at the stocks, at one done and six to do, at the steam, at the sweat. Then all three of them burst out laughing.

'Grand morning!', said the vet, waving the bolt-cutter shears. 'I'll grand morning him. We'll nip up and do him when we've finished this lot.'

It was a gripping performance while it lasted. All the pain inflicted wasn't on the cattle. But occasionally, through the crunching, careering, crashing, banging and blood, and at the end as the vet threw handfuls of sulphonilamide powder at whatever he could reach which was bleeding, he would laugh.

'Thanks,' Jean said. 'Thae beese'll dae now. If they dinnae bleed to death.'

'They won't,' said the vet, doing his best to clean blood and muck off in a bucket of cold water. 'They'll be fine in a day or two. Don't get them with such big horns the next time, eh? Cheerio = grand morning.'

He drove away, laughing.

I clambered out of the heck and into the front seat of the old van. Dad had a final word with Jean then climbed in, stretched, and lit a Players. He puffed out a little smoke, leaving the cigarette in the corner of his mouth as he started the van.

'What were you all laughing at?' I asked.

We bumped out onto the main road, narrowly avoiding a hen, and trundled into third gear round the Collingwood Hotel corner.

'You've got to laugh sometimes,' he replied. 'She'll never make anything off those bullocks, you know.'

He shook his head, wiping one hand down his bib and brace overalls leg.

'Grand morning = I'll say it is.'

The Mill

As we walked up the lonnen from school, between the double row of huge elms where the crows nested, roots peppered by rabbit holes, I could hear a distant roar. It bellowed and sobbed in the darkening afternoon, seeming to pause for breath as a wet, or wrongly placed, sheaf hit the revolving drum.

The Mill

'It's the mill going,' I said excitedly to John as we broke into a trot. Small legs and winter clothes made hard work of the final hill, but we got to the top and stood gasping for breath, watching the mill.

The days of the travelling threshing mill were almost over. The steam engine which used to drive Tommy Carr's mill now stood, blackened and rusting, on waste ground beside our West Road End Field, and that field eventually became known as the Engine Park.

The steam engine had been replaced by a red Massey Harris tractor, which seemed to have a bonnet several yards long. A broad, flat, metal pulley drove the long, wide belt which in turn drove the mill.

This had simplified the job, but not a lot. Much labour was still involved, most of it hard. Sheaves were forked up, cut, and dropped in to the maw of the mill. Straw was baled into massive, unwieldy, parcels tied with wire, which were brutes to handle.

The end where the grain arrived was the business end. Sacks were manhandled off, weighed, and loaded onto trailers. Some farms used a sack-lift. It looked like a large sack barrow, with a metal-grid platform on chains. A sack sat on this and the chains were wound up with a handle, raising the platform to the level of the trailer.

We used the stick and grunt method, two men grasping the top corners of the sack with one hand each and sliding a stout stick underneath the bottom, again each holding this with one hand. Then they grunted and lifted. Some were better at grunting than lifting, and others were desperate to show how strong they were. This combination provided the best results. Two grunters in tandem were painful to watch.

The overall effect, as we stood looking down the back road towards the stacks and the old hayshed, was of noise.

Men sweated and shouted above the roar of the tractor engine and the banging of the mill as they worked. Dinner time and rat hunts provided the only breaks. I liked to be there at a dinner break, listening to the talk, being teased, and eating my paste sandwiches as if I deserved them.

But I didn't like a rat hunt. These came when the last layer or two of sheaves were reached. The men would tie up the bottoms of their trousers with string, or tuck them into their socks, and any women on the gang would straighten up for a breather. Rat hunting was a male occupation.

'There's one!'

'Get the bugger.'

'There!'

'Here!'

'Ouch! Watch that bloody fork.'

'Well, move your foot faster.'

'Christ, there's a nest of them.'

'Where's that dog?'

'Here! Here, you daft brute.'

'He's got it.'

He doesn't miss many.'

'There's another.'

'Get in there. That's one less.'

'Is that them?'

'Can't see any more. Careful with that last sheaf.'

'Here, young 'un – catch!'

And I'd roar with fright as a dead rat was flicked into the air with a fork, towards me. It was soon over. Another stack bottom had been cleared and the mill was roaring remorselessly for the next.

I hovered on the edges of a rat hunt, but liked the dinner time talk of farms they had been to, and farms they didn't want to go back to.

They talked about one local farmer who doled out the dinner money in steadily declining currency. Mill workers had the choice of a meal being provided, which was the old style, or taking two shillings and sixpence in cash. Most opted for the half crown in the hand. Most farmers had a supply of half crowns. But one carried a large bag of small change.

'Aye, the old bugger starts with a shillin'. Then a tanner. Then maybe another tanner.'

'Or two thruppeny bits.'

'Then a thord thruppenny bit.'

'So he's up to two and threepence. He's looking at you, expecting you to say it doesn't matter.'

'And you're still standing with your hand out, thinking bugger you, man, you can afford it better'n me.'

'Then a penny.'

'And he'll poke around in his pouch.'

'As if he's in pain.'

'Like pulling teeth.'

'Looking at you aal the time. Waiting for you to say it doesn't matter about tuppence.'

'But it bloody well does.'

'Finally another penny.'

'Then the ha'pennies.'

'Oh, I don't know if I've got the last ha'penny.'

'He does, ye knaa. Right down to the last ha'penny.'

'And of course he has it.'

'You've jist got to be more hard-necked than him.'

'No wonder the mean old sod makes money.'

Then they'd shake their heads and say what they'd like
to do to him, and burst out laughing. It was wonderful
what you heard about your neighbours from a threshing
gang.

Then there was the bachelor farmer who lived with his
mother. She laid down policy and treated her ageing son as
the odd laddie, despite his best efforts to run the farm
himself.

The gang were having trouble with a main belt which
kept slipping, and the farmer stepped in to help. Sticky
Stockholm Tar was rubbed onto the underside of the belt
with a piece of wood, a sensible move. He then insisted on
helping the belt back into place on the whirling pulley, with
the aid of a fence post.

The post, caught between belt and pulley, flew round
and whapped him on the back of the head before he had
time to get out of the way. The gang, propping each other
up and crying with laughter were wondering what to do
with the unconscious body stretched out on the mud and
chaff, when the mother arrived.

They told her what had happened. There was still no
sign of life. She sniffed.

'Hoy the silly bugger in the shed ower there. He'll be less
bother. And get on with your work.'

They carried him away and got on.

By the time I'd scrambled out of my school clothes and
pulled an old jersey on, it was getting dark. I ran down the
back road as hard as I could, but the dying hum as the
machinery slowed had already started. Pete had cut the
tractor engine, and pulley and mill were winding down.

I got a chorus of good natured abuse.

'You know when to come.'

'Had another easy day, eh?'

'Come on, you can lift this last bag off.'

'That's the one we should have taken off first.'

'I've had enough for one day.'

Dad was helping lift the last of the day's sacks onto a

trailer. He was reasonably pleased with the result.

'Seventy nine bags of Maja barley. Quite a nice sample. Good day at school, boss?'

'Not bad.'

'Best days of your life,' said one of the gang, pulling on an overcoat.

'Don't know you're born,' said another in the dusk.

'Well,' said another voice, 'he soon will. He's got it all to come to.'

'He'll not be doing this anyway,' said the one in the overcoat, waving at the mill. 'This is on its way out. You'll have a combine like the rest of them before long, Mr Maxwell?'

'Maybe,' Dad said, absently, still totting up bags to make sure of his count. 'But it'll not be quite the same as the mill.'

'That'll be right,' said the overcoat. 'The days of slave labour are over.'

They climbed into the old van sent to collect them and it drove away. I walked up towards the steading with Dad as Jake drove the tractor and trailer up.

'It won't be the same,' he said thoughtfully. 'It'll be easier. But . . . it'll be one more of the old jobs gone.'

Potato Planting

We were at the top of the yard filling the tractor with diesel. It carried a drill-plough on the three-point linkage at the back. On this plough, two tin spouts were tied into place with wire and two metal seats jutted into space.

Dad screwed the diesel cap into place and hooked the hose from the tank onto its nail.

He turned to look at the two men standing a few yards away.

'This,' he said, 'might be a little bit tricky.'

Farmers in general are optimists and he was an extreme example. But even he was finding it hard this particular morning, as he set off to plant potatoes.

Potato planting by hand was still practised, but mechanisation was advancing. We had the drill plough, an intermediate stage.

In theory, the system was simple. Two men sat on the back, with seed potatoes in a basket. These were dropped down the spouts into the beds made for them by the passing of the plough.

Fresh supplies of seed were set out in bags at each end of the field. Extra bags were carried on the tractor bonnet in fields where drills were longer.

The tricky bit was to get the spacing right. Potatoes had to be dropped down the spouts at regular intervals, usually twelve to fifteen inches.

Dad had solved the problem of getting this spacing right with a solid metal wheel which trailed behind the plough. Studs were welded to this at various space settings. When a setting had been selected, a spring-loaded bar passed over the stud, gave a dull 'clunk', and a potato was dropped down the spout.

'It's so simple,' Dad said, 'it's almost foolproof.'

He looked at the two waiting workers.

'Well, we'll test it this morning. Come on – jump on.'

He waved and gestured at the two men who looked at him, then looked at each other.

'Geordie' Simpson was one of the more unlikely farm workers. A slightly built, undernourished figure; no amount of sun and wind seemed to colour his white, peaky complexion, half hidden under an oversize cap.

He was gentle and willing, slopping round in wellingtons too big for him, waiting to be pointed at a job. He lived in an old, converted bus which stood in one corner of the yard, eating mainly eggs, sausages and bread and dripping.

Any attempt to change this diet failed. He was the only man I ever knew who added extra salt to home cured bacon.

A man of many jobs, none of them for very long, he had been deafened on a building site when a bucket of cement

fell on his head. No one remarked on any other effect, but I sometimes wondered if the blow which killed his hearing had jumbled his brains.

Now he stood waiting for orders, with the painfully attentive expression he wore when particularly unsure of what he was expected to do.

The Czech stood beside him. One of the war's displaced persons, he lingered in the local hostel, doing casual work. He had a name, but no one could pronounce it. We called him Fred.

He spoke no English except for a random, and staggering, selection of swear words which he used freely. Explaining the process to him would be difficult and getting Geordie to hear the click would be impossible.

'Right,' Dad said, with a cheery confidence he obviously didn't feel, 'let's get on with the job.'

He indicated the two metal seats, one off an old tractor, the other off a horse-drawn hay rake. Both were mounted on sprung-metal bars which bounced as the tractor went down to the Road End field.

Geordie and Fred stotted up and down in silence, except for an occasional expletive over one of the deeper potholes. They had been down earlier with a trailer to set out bags of seed along the headrigs.

'Now then,' Dad said, climbing off the tractor as they dismounted and began to fill their baskets with potatoes. 'This is what you have to do.'

He sat on one of the seats, took a potato from the basket and dropped it down the spout.

'Do that every time this rings.'

He leant down, lifted the solid metal wheel and spun it. To us it sounded like a click. To him it rang like a bell. Either way, the significance of it escaped the labour force.

'Eh?' Geordie said.

'Bugger hell,' said Fred in a tone of polite inquiry.

'Look, it's simple. When the bell rings,' – he pointed at the wheel – 'you drop the potato.' He held up a potato, pointed, and dropped it down the spout.

'Ah,' Geordie breathed.

Fred said something Dad preferred not to hear.

'Fine. Let's get on then.'

He climbed back onto the tractor. It was a Ferguson, one of the small, grey tractors which were an integral part of the farming scene of the 1950s. Simple, reliable, uncluttered, ideal for sowing and planting work, and with that extra something called guts, which meant they pulled more than their weight.

He put it into first gear, of four, and eased the clutch. Sure of his forward direction, he looked over his shoulder to check the staff. Geordie sat holding a potato in his hand with an expectant expression on his face and his head cocked. Fred was shovelling potatoes down the spout as hard as he could.

Dad stopped the tractor. Further explanation was needed. The staff looked up as he got off and came round to the drill plough. Fred popped another two down the spout for good measure.

'No,' Dad said, 'no, no.' He was being patient. 'No, no.

When you hear the bell,' – he pointed at the wheel – 'you drop the potato. Don't put them in so fast,' he said, looking at Fred, 'and you put them in faster, Geordie. Drop them when you hear the bell.'

He emphasised the last few words.

'All right?'

'When ah heor the bell?' asked Geordie.

'Yes, when you hear the bell.'

'Bugger hell,' Fred chipped in.

'Bell,' Geordie bawled across at him.

'Bell,' Dad shouted over his shoulder, as his foot slipped slightly on the clutch and the Fergie jerked into gear and forward.

'Hell,' shouted Fred, ramming potatoes down the spout for dear life.

'Damn,' Dad muttered. He stopped the tractor and leapt

off. The effect was spoiled when his overall leg caught on the footrest and he fell full length on the soft, warm soil. No one thought of laughing as he got to his feet, rubbing his bruised shin and wiping soil off his knees.

He eased the potato from Fred's convulsive grip, held it in one hand and pointed to the wheel with the other.

'When you hear the bell . . . ,' he looked for comprehension, looked in vain, but carried on anyway, '. . . you drop the potato.'

Fred said what seemed to be a Czech word.

'Hear the bell – drop the potato. Right?'

'Damn hell,' Fred said in the affirmative.

'Grand. Right, Geordie?'

'Canny,' he replied.

Dad looked skywards, but apparently found nothing there to cheer him. He got back onto the tractor. We had been there twenty minutes and travelled approximately five yards. I was idly throwing the smallest potatoes from a sack at a rabbit hole.

'And stop doing that,' he called back over his shoulder. 'Two of them putting them in the wrong place is bad enough.'

I stopped. The tractor began to inch forwards. The sun of an April morning was gathering strength in a blue sky. I snuffed at the smell of hessian sack, the dry-earth smell of the seed potatoes, and the moist-earth smell of the soil being split by the drill plough.

Fred roared a rude word. Then another. And a third. He wanted the tractor to stop. Dad stopped. Geordie intent on trying to get the spacing right, by instinct, kept dropping potatoes until Dad shook him by the shoulder. He looked up astonished to find they had stopped.

'What now?'

'Damn blast,' said Fred, pointing at the foolproof patent wheel. A small stone had jammed the spring-loaded bar. There was neither click nor ring.

Dad hit it harder than was necessary with a hammer. He looked at Geordie and had an idea.

'Count to ten every time,' he suggested.

'What?'

'Count – to – ten – then – drop – the – potato.'

'Coont?'

'Aye – count.'

Fred said another rude word.

Dad got back on the tractor. There wasn't the spring in his step that had been there half an hour earlier.

'Here we go again,' he said.

The Fergie moved forward. Geordie sat poised as if about to lay an egg. The tractor stopped.

'Drop it,' Dad bawled.

'Ah was coonting ti ten.'

'Well count faster.'

'Ah canna."

'Well, don't count so many. Count to five.'

'Eh?'

'Count – to – five!'

'Bloody damn five,' said Fred, by way of explanation, using an English word for the first time.

'And you keep your neb out of it,' Geordie shouted on a rising key.

'Bugger, man' Fred exclaimed, sulking back on his seat.

Dad was off the tractor again.

'One more time. Count – to – five. Listen to the bell. Here we go.'

There was only the tick of the tractor engine in the sunlight. It moved forward. Dad looked back. He couldn't believe his eyes. Fred was listening to the click and dropping. Geordie was counting loudly to five and dropping. They were almost in time.

It had really been no bother at all. All it needed was some patience and understanding.

The string round the neck of the bag on the bonnet slipped, and a hundredweight of potatoes fell to the ground in a heap.

First Winter

The year had turned. Christmas had come and gone, briefly back in our old cottage in what used to be my own bed. We had been at the new farm more than four months, and work on the house was no further forward. The fire burned and the gas hissed amiably enough. In a lonesome way I liked it, but it was still the only cheerful room in the house.

It was one reason I liked going across to John's cottage. It was always warm, with a comfortable smell of cooking. While we played, or read, Jake would listen to the wireless or put a Harry Lauder record on the wind-up gramophone. The scratchy, hissing, haunting melody of Roamin' in the Gloamin' would follow me into the darkness as I set off home across the yard.

I was pleased John hadn't died, as I had been sure he

was going to. His mother had kept him off school for a day or two with a cold, and one night I went across the darkened yard to visit.

The fire in his small bedroom was roaring. The heavy curtains were closed and he lay under blankets and an eiderdown, with only his rosy face showing, sweat running down it. As I looked round the door, carrying a book, he spied me. His eyes closed dramatically, he flopped back on the pillow and one hand fell limply out of the cover. I ran home in a panic.

'Dad! Dad! John's going to die.'

'What?'

'He is. He's just lying there. Like this.'

I did a passable impersonation of John's dying swan. Dad straightened up from the kitchen table where he was fretsawing plywood. The fretsaw junior joiner's set had been my Christmas present. In the short time I'd had it, I'd already shown clear signs of an ineptitude with hand tools which would worry him for the rest of his life. He'd taken it over, temporarily.

He went out the back door in a hurry and I walked the floor while he was gone. Prim, the pup, scurried about my feet wagging her tail, but I chased her into her box.

John and I had been through hard times together in the past few months, notably when we persevered in setting fire to a heap of damp wheat straw with some matches we had borrowed from Jake. Unfortunately, Jake didn't know we'd borrowed them and the wheat straw was in the wooden-stalled byre. The wood was slightly charred and we were lightly walloped.

I was walloped, not for setting fire to straw, a pyromaniac tendency I inherited from my grandfather, but for lying about it.

'Did you set fire to the straw?'

'No.'

'Well, who did?'

'I don't know.'

'Was it John?'

The temptation was strong to say yes.

'No.'

'I know you did it. Why?'

'I didn't do it.'

That was when he lost his temper and made a grab for me, a happening so unusual that I panicked, scrambled through an open window at the front of the house, and roosted up one of the bigger apple trees, until it got dark and I got cold.

He was hand-drilling a hole in a fork-shank to put a new bolt through, and looked up as I stood forlornly in the doorway.

'Did you do it?'

'Yes.'

He gave me one smart clout on the back of my bare legs.

'Ow!'

'Don't tell lies. Do you want some tea?'

Now he came back into the kitchen. I looked at him anxiously.

'Is he dead?'

'No, he's all right. No wonder he was lying like that. It's like a ship's boiler room in there. I've told his mother to open the window and door, and put the fire out. Poor wee soul, his temperature must be about a hundred and ten.'

'Are you sure he's all right?'

'Of course he's all right. He was keeking at me out of one eye while I was talking to his mother. He'll be fine if he gets the chance to cool down.'

He went back to the fretwork and I picked up *The Dandy Annual*. For him it was a brief respite in a headlong four months of harvesting, ploughing, drilling and fertilising.

Valuers for both sides had agreed an ingoing payment of less than £1000 because the farm was in such poor, starved condition, badly fenced and drained and in immediate need of care and attention.

He thought about nothing else.

'What I want to do is grow three year's crops at once. Do you know what that lorry driver said the other day? That

there'd been more fertiliser up this road in the past month
than in the past ten years.'

About two hundred tons of ground limestone went on to
sweeten neglected soils. Grass fields got six hundredweights
an acre of compound fertiliser. He bought a new David
Brown tractor for £505, a figure I couldn't grasp.

Then we went to Coupland farm sale and bought a two-
wheeled, flat bottomed bogie for £30, a small cart for £19,
one hundred fence posts for £8, a henhouse for £16.10
shillings and an oil tank for £3.10 shillings.

It seemed a lot to invest in second-hand goods. The
finances of the business were beginning to impress themselves on me, and I was a boy who worried.

'That's a lot of money,' I said, thinking it was time for a
cautionary word.

'I think we'll manage,' he replied. 'I quite enjoy signing

my own cheques – as long as they're small ones.'

We joined the queue of farmers waiting to pay for what they had bought. Almost all of them simply signed their name, some with difficulty, and passed the chequebook over to the clerk. He then brought out a sheet of paper from a pigeon hole behind him, with the farmer's name at the top and list of what he had bought, with prices. The clerk made out the cheque to the mart, filled in the amount to be paid, and usually the counterfoil as well.

When it came to our turn, the clerk politely held his hand out for the chequebook and Dad, equally politely declined.

'No thanks. I'll do it. How much was it again?'

He knew, because he'd written it down in his Lever's Cattle Foods diary as he bid, but there was always the possibility of a mistake or misunderstanding in the hustle and bustle of a farm sale. This was particularly true of smaller items, with the auctioneer bursting to get on and farmers shouting good humoured insults to each other about the quality of what friends were bidding for.

There was no mistake. He carefully made the cheque out for £77, signed Thos. F. Maxwell even more carefully, and handed it over. I felt part of big business.

We recouped the farm sale outlay, and a large part of the tractor, the following week. It was our first visit to Cornhill mart, a stone building, standing close to the railway station.

Stock could be brought in, or more usually taken out, by train. As one of the nearest farms to the mart, we walked the cattle down early in the morning. It was raw cold, with a touch of frost, and the breath of the massive, slow-moving cattle hung in the air. We were happy to see them move slowly. It meant they weren't getting excited and neither were we. They walked quietly into one of the dozens of inter-locking pens and we went back to sell them later.

It wasn't a big sale, but there were several local farmers at the ringside as well as butchers and dealers, including our acquaintance who had had cattle in the Quarry Field. He looked beefier, with trousers more half-mast than ever;

he grunted and turned away. That might have been expected, but an oddity which affected Dad for some time was that hardly anyone else spoke to him either.

At Alnwick mart everyone knew him. Last time, in the space of my cheese sandwich from the snack bar, six people stopped to talk. I remembered it well because the second one gave me a threepenny bit, and I looked hopefully at each new face wondering if another chunky brass coin was going to come my way.

Football, Home Guard, Young Farmers' activities, local dances, selling cattle and sheep every week, made him well known. At Cornhill he seemed to have become invisible.

'They know who I am all right,' he said, with a surprising amount of bitterness. 'Well, I can do without them.'

The prices made by the cattle helped a little. They were Irish-bred crosses of indeterminate age, weighing more than 13 hundredweights each and probably in debt to one of their many owners during the course of their long lives. It didn't seem to be us, and he was pleased with an average price of more than £75 each.

'Those cattle sold well today,' he said, working at the small fretwork vice fixed to the war-time utility kitchen table.

'Yes,' I said from the depths of a Desperate Dan story.

'I was looking at those two sows I bought before Christmas – I don't think they're in pig after all.'

'Oh?'

'No, I'm going to have to get them served again. I'll see if I can get Peter Wight's boar from Marldown.'

These tended to be one-sided conversations. I picked up a little more each day, but never enough.

He worked away at the fretwork with the slender-bladed saw.

'I've ordered a beet topper and a single-furrow plough from Elders.'

'That's good.'

'There should be 300 fence posts and three big gate posts

coming this week.'

'Right.'

'I'll have to clean the Fordson pipes out tomorrow. It keeps cutting out.'

'That's bad.'

'Old bitch. But I'll get it fixed. Are you off to bed?'

'Just a minute. I'm finishing Desperate Dan.'

'He's some man, Desperate Dan.'

'I didn't like to tell him I always thought there was a resemblance, especially the chin.

'I've cancelled the potato planter at Jackson's. I'll not deal with them any more – the bill comes every day.'

'That's no use.'

'No, it isn't. Right, off to bed. I'll be through in a wee while.'

'Are you sure John's all right?'

'Yes. He'll be up and about in a day or two.'

'Goodnight.'

'Goodnight, son.'

I left him cutting a cunning curve round the plywood and went to bed.

First Spring

We burst out of winter and into spring like calves turned out to grass, heels in the air and trying to run in several directions at the same time.

Not that the later winter months had been idle. A wooden hut at Little Mill had been bought and dismantled over four days. We brought the good timber home and burned the fragments, splinters, chunks of roofing felt and rotten sleepers. The burning creosote smell lingered and eddied on the January air, and in my mind for ever.

At the farm we built a shed, the first reputable one to go up in living memory. It was built with asbestos sheets on the same lines as a Nissan hut, half hexagon instead of half moon. The asbestos sheets mounted on dwarf brick walls, glistened pure white on the skyline.

We laid the floors with concrete, mixed using gravel from the Tweed banks which we carted ourselves with the small trailer.

I looked at the building taking shape.

'Why is the top half higher than the bottom half?'

'That's a point – maybe they've made a mistake. Or we have.'

'No we haven't! Why is it higher?'

'It's a wonderful plan to save labour. Top half – store potatoes, barley and fertiliser.'

'You'll not get them all in. It's not that big a shed.'

'Not all at once. At different times of the year. The bottom half will be the tractor shed and workshop.'

'That's a good idea.'

'And it's on a lower level so that lorries can reverse in and load or unload without a lot of lifting.'

'That's clever.'

'That's what I thought,' he said.

The estate still procrastinated about what they would do to the house. My mother and the other four children, with a fifth on the way, were still at Ivy Cottage. We travelled up and down most weekends, often with supplies, always with eggs.

Some Saturday nights we carried more eggs than others. Some nights we went faster than others. One night eggs and speed coincided at the Blue Bell corner.

'I didn't like the sound of that,' he said, as we hurtled round the corner. There was a series of loud cracking noises, followed by squelching as the collie jumped up and trampled in it.

'Lie down,' he shouted over his shoulder, slowing down and pulling in to the side. Shouting 'Lie down' had been a mistake, as we discovered when we opened the back doors on a large omelette with Fan obediently lying in a large pool of yolks.

'We've broken some,' I said in excitement, with a gift for stating the obvious which has never left me.

47

'I'd guessed that,' he said briefly, starting to scrape out as much of the mess as he could. We tried to clean down the collie and soak up the rest with an old sack. Old hessian doesn't absorb much. With concentrated effort, and a fair amount of ingenuity, we managed to spread egg yolk over most of the van. The collie had more on her when we finished than when we started. I had considerably more than when I started, and was beginning to feel sick. We gave it up as a bad job and drove away from what, after that, was always Egg Corner. I liked telling people about it, but Dad never seemed to share my enthusiasm.

By the end of January everything has been threshed out of the stacks. The Engine Park stack had been estimated at 160 sacks and produced 104. That was bad. But another produced 143 sacks instead of 120 estimated, and sold at

£8.12s.6d per quarter.

'Is four times that a ton?'

'No, five.'

I struggled with this.

'But there's four quarters in a whole. We've just been doing it with Mrs Whittle.'

'There are in most things. But not in a ton of barley. There's five.'

'That's just stupid.'

'I get paid more if there's five quarters than if there were four.'

'That's good then.'

'Yes, that's good.'

We riddled out a small outdoor pit of potatoes together. Jake had broken his ankle, stumbling over a rolling turnip while laying them out in the field for sheep, and was off work for eight weeks.

We persevered with the potatoes in cold weather. I stood at the end where the bags were filling, peering over the top to switch the shutter when one was full.

At the far end, almost hidden by the blue smoke coming from the two-stroke engine, Dad piled several graipfulls of potatoes on as fast as he could. Then he ran round the corner of the rattling, shaking riddle to watch them come up the rollers, picking off any rotten ones. When I shouted that a bag was full, he came along, whisked it off, put an empty sack on, and went back to shovel some more. Every ten bags or so we stopped to weigh and tie them, and a lorry came in for a five ton load.

Spring was already in the air. As the nights got lighter, he couldn't sit still. If he sat on a chair, he twitched and had to be up and doing something. Towards the end of February, 180 month-old chicks were delivered, and we sowed beans in the Windmill Field, followed by barley in the House Field, Three Corner Field, Engine Park and Little Baldrons, with Sun Two oats in the Fox Cover and Star oats in the Pond End. On March 18th we finished.

'First in the district,' he claimed, and started work on the

A Farmer's Boy

lambing shed.

We drilled sugar beet in the Road End field. I steered the little grey Fergie at snail's pace, while he walked behind, checking that all four seed boxes, with their little rubber belts, were working and spacing out the seed correctly. I felt there was nothing we couldn't do together.

But times were changing. Work on the house finally got under way. That was only after Mum and the rest of the family moved into the same shambles as they could have moved into back in September. Which was more or less what she said, while supervising the unpacking and unloading.

An Aga cooker and boiler were installed in the kitchen, which became, as in almost every farmhouse, the focus of all activity. And foot traffic.

'Shut that door!' was the other necessary favourite, particularly on wet and windy days when we seemed to change our mind more often.

'It's a proper bugger, Alice,' said Norman, the coalman, sympathising with her over a cup of tea, after he had unloaded a ton of coke for the Aga, and a ton of coal into the lean-to shed. He watched, eyes glinting in a blackened face, his bald head shining like an egg, with his cap on his knee, as two children got half in the door. Mum started to turn round, and they scurried out again.

Norman took another sip of tea, the cup dwarfed in his hands, as Dad looked round the door to check the delivery.

'Hello, Tommy,' Norman said, with his nasal voice, 'I was just saying kids are a proper bugger in this weather. The little buggers won't stay in or stay oot.'

Dad nodded warningly towards three of us who happened to be in the kitchen.

'Mind the swearing,' he said.

'Swearing!' said Norman, 'The little buggers have never said a word while I've been here. I'll have to get on Alice. Thanks for the tea. Just the bloody job on a day like this. Cheerio, Tommy.'

'He doesn't know he's doing it,' Mum said.

50

'Well, he bloody well should,' Dad said over his shoulder, closing the door quickly behind him.

He was pleased to have us all under one roof again, fires burning, bedrooms filled, meals on the table, the house taking shape at the same time as the farm. Life and energy was throbbing through us with the same steady thud as the new diesel generator, which produced electricity to replace the old gas mantles. We were on our way.

Prim

There were sometimes more than two dogs on the farm, but never less. We always had at least two collies – one which worked and one which didn't. Occasionally, neither of them worked, but that was accidental. One of them should have done.

The one which never worked, and wasn't expected to, was an ornamental Shetland collie by the full name of Harelaw Primadonna, the only pedigree livestock I was ever involved with.

She was smaller than the working Border collies, black and gold, with a gentle nature and a broader than usual head and muzzle for the breed. Dad would look at her fondly and admire the head.

'That's what a Sheltie's head should look like. Not some of these narrow faced little ferrets you see going about. Good dog, Trip.'

How he got to Trip from Harelaw Primadonna was a small mystery, but I never heard her called anything else. He was concerned that modern fad breeding was removing the brains from the Shetland. It took some time to find a dog with a suitably broad head and, presumably, brains, to mate with her. But one was found and Trip had pups, as quietly and gently as she did everything else.

It upset the house cat briefly. That was Judy, the only house cat we ever had, and the fastest cat in the county through a door. This was explained by the fact that in palmier days for her, when there had been fewer children and only a friendship with Trip to worry about, she had been in the habit of following Dad about.

Walking through from the back kitchen one windy day he had slammed the door behind him, to cut off as much of the draught as possible. He did this effectively and also removed half Judy's tail. The neat amputation sent her round the living room like a furry tortoiseshell jumping jack. From then on she approached open doors with crouching suspicion, braced herself for seconds, then made a creditable effort to break the sound barrier as she went through.

The mewling and puling of the new pups upset her for a day or two, put she was soon snuggling in among them.

I was fascinated, not by the cat whose behaviour seemed no odder than usual, but by the blind pups.

There were five of them and, as happens when you watch young animals closely, what at first seemed like five identical bald faces, blind eyes and open mouths seeking a teat, quickly became five individuals.

The clearest difference was between the biggest and smallest. From the beginning I wanted the big one. He was more lively, drank faster, made more noise and opened his eyes more quickly. At an early stage he was boss pup and I was going to keep him as my own. I'd never had a pet before, unless I counted two or three goldfish from the Hirings Fair, which expired as quickly as I won them.

Rex was different. Like a proud father I had his future planned out before his eyes were quite open, and in the career stretching before him he missed out on very little open to a dog of good looks and character.

Three of the pups were quickly sold, leaving Rex and the little one at a few weeks old. I was playing with them on the kitchen floor one evening after tea, the increasingly boisterous Rex and the timid, podgy little bitch, when Dad came in.

'I've got an offer for the pup,' he said.

'Oh?', I answered, turning the little bitch over and

tickling her stomach. The small legs kicked and jerked and the still almost hairless tail waved about. Then Rex came barging in, knocking her sideways, demanding attention, head up and tail going like a semaphore signal.

'Yes,' he said, cautiously I thought. 'The only trouble is . . .'

I don't think it's instinct. I've always had a knack of jumping to the worst possible conclusion, and occasionally I'm right.

'Not Rex!' I yelled. 'Not Rex!'

Both pups shot for cover and Trip sat bolt upright in her box where she had been drowsing. Judy did what cats do when there's trouble in the air. She padded quietly to the door, paused and crouched, and shot through with a scutter of claws on old linoleum.

'Afraid so,' he said. 'I was talking to Selby Morton the lorry man from Wooler. He's looking for a good dog.'

'Aw, not Rex,' I bawled, trying to grab him, but he was alarmed and hid beside his mother. Two small faces looked out of the box at me.

'Sorry,' he said, as briskly as possible to get my mind off it. 'He's offering a good price.'

'How much?'

'Seven pounds.'

I couldn't compete with that. I had a large collection of small coloured stones, pieces of old crockery and several dark blue fragments of Milk of Magnesia jars hoarded in a tin, But very little money.

I thought of continuing to bawl, but it was becoming an outdated tactic. Dad continued to be brisk.

'I said we'd take him along tonight. I'll just have a wash and put my jacket on.'

I sat in a steely sulk all the way to Selby's house. Rex wet on my trousers in excitement and I thought it served Dad right. I was soaking wet and it was his fault.

After we had knocked and gone in, the fox came to meet us, brush up and inquisitive. It was half grown and glossy. It ran round the kitchen after sniffing at Rex, then climbed possessively into its basket. Selby gave Dad the seven pounds and me a shilling. Then we drove home. It was my first lesson in economics.

I didn't like it any more than the later ones. The sulk was still going strong as Dad put the kettle on and reached for the cups to make cocoa. He put two spoonfuls in, mixed it with a spoonful of sugar and added the water. The spoon he left in mine threatened to stay upright, and I glowered at it.

'Isn't there any milk?'

'No,' he said, buttering two thick slices of bread. 'The cow's drying up and Mrs Wilkinson needed another couple of pints tonight.'

'So I haven't got any milk?'

'Not much,' he said, tipping the last of it from the jug. 'But you've got a friend.'

The little bitch was creeping across the floor to the sound of my voice.

'Huh!'

I took a swig of cocoa and my eyes started to water. Dad swallowed a mouthful of his with no ill-effects and bit into his bread and butter contentedly.

'That'll put hairs on your chest,' he grinned.

'Huh!'

Once into a good sulk I didn't like to waste it. He shrugged and picked up the Farmers' Weekly. I risked another sip of cocoa. Well mixed with bread and butter, the taste grew on you. Not fast, but it grew.

I felt something soft against my feet and looked down. The little pup looked up, tail thumping the floor.

What're we going to call her?'

'Call who?' he asked innocently, looking up from A. G. Street's weekly column.

'This,' I replied, swinging the pup off the floor. She gave a startled squeak and wriggled briefly, then sat on my bare knee.

'That is Harelaw Primrose. I thought we could call her Prim for short.'

'Prim? I think I like that.'

Prim wagged her tail harder as I patted her head.
'Yes. Prim's not bad at all.'

Bangour

In our second winter at the farm I went down twice with
pneumonia in the space of six weeks. It was years before I
realised that pleural pneumonia didn't mean you had to
have it twice.

It seemed serious at the time, particularly to me when
the nurse gave the penicillin injections. There's nowhere to
run in a hospital. They always get you in the end. She
certainly did.

I recovered quickly, but Fiona's recovery from a brain-
tumour operation later in the same year took much longer.
Much of her early recovery time was spent at Bangour
Hospital, on the other side of Edinburgh.

We made the long car journey, as a family, on many
Sundays. The car was a large, black, second-hand Humber
Hawk which had replaced the old blue Morris as the family
grew, physically and numerically.

We played I-Spy. This often foundered on differences of
opinion on spelling.

'I spy with my little eye something beginning with . . .
with . . . wuh.'

'Are you sure that's what it starts with?'

'Yes.'

'All right – window.'

'No.'

'Watch.'

'No.'

'Windscreen wiper.'

'No.'

'Look, are you sure it starts with wuh?'

'Yes . . . I think so.'

'Whisper it to me . . . what! No, that doesn't start with
wuh. It starts with a duh!'

'How can she get a wuh and a duh mixed up?'
Mum looked round from the front seat.
'Can't you say W and D?'
'Well, if she can't tell the difference between wuh and duh she isn't likely to know a W either.'

'This game's just stupid. Really stupid.'
'Not if you can spell, idiot.'
'Well, she can't.'
'No, but she's trying hard. Let's have one more go.'
'All right. You go. You can spell.'
'Right. I spy with my little eye . . .'
'We don't have to say that every time.'
There was a chorus of complaint.
'Yes we do. That's the rules.'
'All right then. Say it if you have to.'
'I spy with my little eye, something beginning with . . .

let me see . . . with . . . duh.'
  'Are you sure?'
  'I can spell, you know.'
  'Door.'
  'No.'
  'Driver.'
  'No.'
  'Dad.'
  'No = that's the same thing.'
  'Dress.'
  'No."
  'Is it in the front or the back?'
  'It's not in the car.'
  'But it's got to be in the car.'
  'Well, it's not.'
  'If it's not in the car, how can you spy with your little eye?'
  'It was beside the road back there.'
  'This game's just really stupid. He doesn't know how to play.'
  'I do. It was a dog.'
  Mum turned round again as voices rose higher.
  'Why don't you play something else?'
  Dad half-looked over his shoulder, at the heaving, smouldering group on the back seat, digging elbows into each other and snarling. He had a fair tenor voice, church choir trained, and occasionally sang on the return journeys.
  'Why not sing something?'
  'What?'
  'I don't know. You get singing at school sometimes, don't you?'
  We did, usually last thing on a Friday afternoon. Our new head teacher, Miss Larson, put a lot of emphasis on group activity.
  She was learning to temper enthusiasm with caution. Older boys, looking forward to weekend freedom, were not the best group to sing a line which went : 'Here we sit like birds in the wilderness.'

They put tremendous gusto into this line, with the subtle addition of one letter, bawling it out while those of us at the front warbled away dutifully. Miss Larson said nothing, but listened attentively, and we didn't sing 'Down in Demerara' again, despite frequent requests from music-lovers at the back.

Another dropped from the repetoire was 'Jubilate' which rhymed surprisingly well with 'Ruby Larson.' Oh yes, we got singing, but I didn't know if Dad would appreciate some of the finer phrasing.

We tried 'Camptown Races', which had had me crying with laughter the first time I sang it, but not enough of us knew the words. We gave up singing, which never seemed as much fun in daylight anyway, and fell back on checking numberplates on passing cars. We each had a letter and the one with the highest count won. That took us to Bangour.

The first Sunday we made the journey, we broke the return trip at Uncle Dave's house on the outskirts of Edinburgh. He came to the door as we piled out onto the pavement, five of us under our own steam and Mum carrying the baby.

Aunt Jeanne had tea set out for us. At that time they had no children of their own, and the plate of sandwiches had been thinly cut and tastefully arranged. A succession of small paws cleared it in less than two minutes. We had had a long afternoon. Biscuits and a small cake went the same way in less time. Dad nursed a cup of tea and Uncle Dave and Aunt Jeanne glanced thoughtfully at each other.

The following Sunday there were two plates of sand-wiches, piled higher, with some scones to follow before we reached the biscuits. It took us slightly longer, but we got there in impressive style without a pause for breath. Dad chipped in with one or two sandwiches. Uncle Dave and Aunt Jeanne exchanged even more thoughtful glances.

Mum warned us as we turned into Davidson's Mains on the third Sunday.

'Don't be greedy. We're not here to eat them out of house and home."

'Aw, Mum, we're hungry.'

'You shouldn't be – if you'd eaten more breakfast.'

'We don't eat that much.'

'You did. You had a sandwich in each hand last week.'

'Just because Katrine was going to take the one I wanted.'

'Well, don't do that. There's plenty for everyone.'

'But there isn't.'

'Only because they've never seen anything like you lot before. Don't grab. And don't be greedy.'

We disembarked once more on the pavement. A curtain twitched and the door opened. We trooped in to find double the number of sandwiches, scones, cakes and biscuits.

We didn't give up easily, but one by one the contenders fell away. As small jaws gradually stopped moving and small hands stopped reaching out, Uncle Dave sat forward more eagerly on the edge of his chair. He looked across at Aunt Jeanne and nodded, as I reached for one more sandwich. I had got as far as biscuit and cake, but was quite happy to drop back to basics.

I chewed the sandwich without much enthusiasm. It hadn't the piquancy of those I'd eaten before starting on the cake. Dad picked up the last piece of gingerbread. Mum, occupied until then as usual by the demands of smaller children, made a late sortie on the sandwiches. Uncle Dave's eagerness gave way to a slight frown. This relaxed as Dad sat back. It returned as my hand hovered over the plate. It relaxed as I dropped my hand and went back to my chair. He jumped to his feet.

'Beaten you this time,' he cried, rubbing his hands together. 'I didn't think it could be done. But we've done it.'

Driving home in darkness, Mum turned round in the front seat.

'I told you not to eat them out of house and home.'

'We didn't. There was some left.'

'That's right,' Dad said. 'There was. Dave didn't mind. He was quite pleased to get the better of them.'

We left the lights of Dalkeith behind, heading towards the steep rise of Soutra Hill.

'I thought Fiona was much better today,' Dad said.

'Yes, she was talking a bit more.'

'It was funny when she said banana when she meant tomato.'

'She knew what she meant,' Dad said. 'She just couldn't quite get the right word. But she's much better.'

One or two of the smaller ones were sleeping, one on Mum's knee.

'What about that song Calamity Jane was singing?'

'The Deadwood Stage?'

'No, the other one – what was it?'

'Secret Love?' Mum suggested.

'No, the really good one – Black something.'

'Take Me Back to the Black Hills?'

'That's it. That's a good one. Let's sing that.'

Three of us were singing. We sang it several times.

'Take me back to the Black Hills, the Black Hills of Dakota, and the beautiful Indian country that I love, Lost my heart to the Black Hills . . .'

As we came over Soutra, turning off at Carfraemill Hotel for the final long run home, we started it, drowsily, for the seventh or eighth time. As I started to drop off to sleep I heard Dad from the front seat.

'When I first heard it, I liked that song.'

School

'It's barring out the morn. Get here early.'

'Eh?'

'Barring oot.'

'What?'

He looked down at me as if I was a half-wit. I felt like one because I had no idea what Johnny was talking about.

'Just get in early and you'll see. Mind out the way.'

He pushed me aside from where I'd just reached the top of the queue for a turn on the strip of frozen ice, which stretched half the length of the school yard. He took a short run and launched himself on to it, zooming down, arms out for balance, reaching the far end at full speed and running off onto solid ground to stop himself falling over.

'Hey . . .'

I was so busy watching him, someone else had pushed past and I'd lost my turn. As one of the youngest I had to go a long way down the queue to find someone softer to push in front of. I was small, impressionable and easily worried by someone who was big, strong and fourteen. That was Johnny, sauntering away from the end of the slide towards the bigger boys. They'd monopolised the slide for most of the morning break and were now having a breather, allowing the rest of us a turn before the bell rang. Which it did, as I finally made my delayed run-up, but I kept running anyway.

My knees were already raw from the times I'd fallen over, my hands were grazed and my cheeks were glowing. Speed was travelling over polished ice on tackity boots, and success was staying upright long enough to reach the far end.

We all wore tackity boots, except one or two incomers who favoured shoes. Most of us came from surrounding farms, where our fathers wore the same kind of footwear – solid, black leather with metal tackits cobbled into the bottom, and half-moon metal strips at front and back which, on hard road, made us sound like small ponies. Losing a curved metal strip was like casting a shoe.

With tackits, we could kick sparks off concrete and lumps off each other playing football, although they were a liability when it came to the infrequent country-dancing lessons. Not for us, but for the girls in gingham checks and pigtails who partnered us, both sides showing the greatest reluctance.

I hated dancing, a feeling shared by anyone I was unlucky enough to partner.

'How do I always have to dance with you?' Sheena asked. She was one of Johnny's younger sisters and came from a family which could take care of themselves.

'I don't want to dance with you either,' I said gallantly.

'Well, watch your feet. Please, miss, he's stood on my foot again.'

'It was her fault, miss. She's going too fast.'

'It's supposed to be fast. You're just too slow.'

She accompanied this with a fierce jab to the ribs and we stood glaring at each other. There were tackit marks on her white ankle sock, clear indication of a foul tackle.

'You're not playing football now,' she continued. 'You're absolutely clumsy.'

I couldn't argue with that. So many people had told me

the same thing so often it must be true. I flushed and she said, more kindly, 'Let's try again.'

We trampled and stumbled round until the music ended, or at least I did while Sheena did her best to keep her feet out of the way, before parting with a sigh of mutual relief. I wasn't alone in having two left feet, both in heavy boots. There was general relief when sandshoes were decreed for PT lessons and dancing. We danced as badly as ever, but our partners didn't suffer so much.

But for sliding on ice, boots were essential. There was nothing quite like gliding down the slide in the frosty air, that morning with the last clang of the bell still sounding on it. Or there wasn't, as I coasted towards the end, until Harry and Les, also fitting in a last run, crashed into, and piled over, me. We limped into the classroom, muttering at each other.

'What's barring out?' I whispered to Vincent. But Mr Cunningham turned round from the blackboard and I stopped.

I didn't get there early next morning. We had a difficult start, with a load of lime arriving unexpectedly, and being too frozen to come out of the lorry. Children not going to school got involved with those of us who were. One child spilled a plate of porridge which another one stood in. I was saved by that morning's postman. Against all regulations he opened the back doors of his van and we clambered in.

We looked out through the grilled back windows, bouncing on mailsacks, and imagined we were going to jail. The playground was unnaturally quiet as he let us out, beside the post office. The yard was empty, the slide unused despite the frost, and there was no noise and chatter. We weren't that late, the school bell couldn't have rung. It was strange.

We walked up the few steps at the front of the school, and round the corner to the boys' cloakroom door. It was locked. Not only that, desks and chairs were pilled up against it from the inside. There was a voice from a window.

'You're late. Get round the back.'

'What . . .'

'Get round the back. He'll be here in a minute.' We got round the back into the girls' playground. A window was opened and we were hauled in, fast and roughly, scraping my already damaged knees on the stonework and landing head-first on the pitted wooden floorboards of the infant classroom. Everyone else, about 30 of them, was already there, laughing and talking. Desks and chairs were piled up against all doors and watch was being kept on the windows.

'Here he is,' someone called.

And there he was, outside the door, shaking the handle with a set expression on his face. It didn't offer to open. He swung round and walked away with short, brisk steps to try another door. He rattled that with no result except a roar of laughter from inside. I laughed with the rest, but I couldn't help feeling, as I'd heard my grandmother say, that I'd soon be laughing on the other side of my face.

I remembered the morning the hunt had come within earshot of the village. It was almost playtime when the eerie horn-blast whispered on the wind into the classroom.

The coke stove, round which coats and gloves were hung to steam and half-dry on wet mornings, had been particularly soporific. Heads were nodding in the thick air, but now they shot up like alert tortoises and ears pricked for the next blast of the horn. It came, and the fidgeting started. Boots shuffled and pawed the floor under desks, books rustled in agitation, and eyes turned to the clock.

Mr Cunningham turned away from the blackboard towards his desk. He lifted the lid and meditatively withdrew the flexible cane.

'Some of you may think I'm getting a little deaf in my old age.'

He made a gentle, swishing noise with the cane.

'I can assure you I'm not.'

He was a small, sturdy man with glasses and neat, firm hands who could draw trees and bowls of fruit in pastel chalks on grey sugar paper with amazing ease and speed.

'Anyone thinking of following the hounds . . .,' he said and paused, '. . . would be making a mistake. I think you know what I mean.'

He took a practice swing with the cane, tapped it on the desk, and slipped it back inside. There was a nervous titter from the front rows and silence from the back. Then the muttering and shuffling started again, as playtime was declared, and we filed out. The big lads went into a huddle straight away, which didn't last long. Another blast of the hunting horn echoed on the wind from the East Learmouth direction. Johnny sniffed the air, like a fox himself, the fair curly hair bristling, then he was gone, running, past the ruined cottages and over the small wall into the road. After a slight hesitation three more followed. Two others looked sheepishly at each other, then came across to barge around more than necessary in the kick about several of us had started.

The four didn't come back until next morning, and Mr Cunningham emphasised his view that they had made a mistake by giving up the pleasures of the classroom for the hard work of following fox, horses and hounds on foot cross-country for hours. He caned them hard and systematically and, one by one, they walked back to their seats to clutch their hands between their thighs, or tuck them under their armpits, according to inclination. When the whack of stick on flesh stopped singing round the room, we all got on with our work. I scribbled away for dear life for what seemed like hours before I looked up. I thought that as he had got himself nicely warmed up, Mr Cunningham might feel like keeping in practice and I wanted to give him no excuse.

Now, it seemed to me, in the barred-in classroom, watching the barred-out teacher, that this might be an excuse for a mass caning. Flogging, they called it in *Tom Brown's Schooldays*, but a caning from Cunningham seemed bad enough.

I wasn't the only one worried. There was a commotion at one side of the room and mixed howls of laughter and disgust as a space cleared round Ernie. He stood alone, miserably, with his pudding-basin haircut, his grey shorts held up by braces which were beginning to stretch under the strain. Like me he was new to barring out. He also had a problem.

'All right,' he said defiantly, jerking his head. 'I've shit mesel again.'

'Shit myself,' said one of the older girls automatically, blushing at the renewed howl of laughter as she realised what she had said.

'Well, yi knaa it's not funny then,' Ernie said coolly. 'A'll have ti gaan. It'll be on the floor soon.'

He waddled towards the door and no one tried to get in his way. There was a clatter of opening windows, and an even more frantic clatter of desks and chairs as we cleared a path for him to reach the great outdoors. We had to do this because the toilets, the dry closet type, were outside. As we fought to get Ernie out, inviting him to stay at a distance until the door was open, Mr Cunningham was fighting to get in.

'Giving up this year, eh?' he puffed, pushing at the door. 'Not like you lads.'

'No sir,' Johnny shouted, feverishly heaving another desk out of the way, 'it's Ernie, sir, he's . . . he's . . .'

'Shit mesel, sir,' Ernie called helpfully over the crowd.

'What! What did that boy say.'

'He's messed himself sir,' Les shouted, hauling the last desk out of the way.

'Where's the key,' Robert shouted, jerking the handle.

'Here, here,' called a voice from the back, throwing it forward. With trembling fingers, Robert unlocked the cloakroom door and hurled himself back. Outside, Mr Cunningham also stepped back. Ernie waddled forward again, one hand clutching his shorts, the other waving forlornly in the air, looking like a small, sorry creature from the Black Lagoon.

'All right,' said Mr Cunningham when Ernie had been sent home under an escort of two of the older girls, walking at a safe distance. 'You get your afternoon off.'

A roar went up. Soon, all the desks and chairs had been carried and shunted back into place, our voices rising and falling on a swell of laughter and chatter.

'But,' he added. 'after Ernie's . . . er . . . unfortunate accident, which put rather a dampener on things . . . we may have to think again about barring out.'

Cries of 'Oh no sir,' filled the air. Barring out, I had now discovered, involved giving a present to the teacher in return for a half-day holiday and barring him out to make certain he agreed. It had gone on, taken in good part by both sides, for as long as anyone could remember.

'We'll see,' he said. 'Now let's get some work done this morning. And would you mind opening another window or two. It's rather stuffy in here.'

'What are you doing home,' my mother asked, after we'd wandered up the lonnen at dinner-time.

'We've got a half day holiday.'
She frowned slightly.
'I didn't know anything about that?'

'We were only told this morning.'
'What happened?'
'Not much. We locked the doors and piled the desks up against them to keep Mr Cunningham out.'
'What!'
'Oh and Ernie dirtied his pants and had to go home.'
'What!'
'And I think I've lost the round metal bit off the front of my boot.'
'I worry about you sometimes,' she said. 'Do you want any dinner?'

Sow

We had a simple pig-keeping system. About ten sows ran

with the boar in a grass paddock, living in huts made from posts, netting and straw. When they farrowed, piglets ran outside with their mothers until eight, nine or ten weeks old. This time depended on when a squad could be organised to bring them inside.

Ten week old, free-range piglets are lively, agile and noisy. We had many a happy hour getting them into the fattening shed, without being eaten by agitated sows.

It wasn't much of a shed, but the best we could do at the time. It had been built in the distant past, from sleepers and asbestos and used, as far as we could see, as a stable. Double stalls were converted into pig pens and the growing inhabitants were fed barley meal and steamed potatoes.

The floury barley meal was ground up by the lethal-looking hammermill. This sat opposite the granary door and was driven by a long belt on a pulley, from the Fordson tractor. The lethal part was inching past it to get through the door, the belt humming, the mill zooming, with an occasional clang when a small stone hit the grinding plates.

Pigs ate the meal and drank their water keenly enough, but they loved potatoes. The steamer stood on three metal legs, with a fire blazing in the bottom. Potatoes steamed in the top section. Although supposed to be unfit for human consumption, they made the shed smell like a school canteen. I didn't mind a mouthful from the better ones and the pigs loved them.

The trick was to tip the potatoes quickly into their trough and reverse rapidly. As I reversed, they charged in. Snouts went straight into the trough. And straight out again, sniffing for cool air. Down again. Up again. The more adventurous would pull a potato out and toss it in the air like a tyro juggler, dropping it on the pen floor. They would then run round it suspiciously, making little darts to test the temperature. As they prepared for a final dash to swallow it, another pig would leave the trough and grab it from under their nose. It's surprising how much bafflement a pig's face can show.

The sows had a more varied diet than the fattening pigs.

This was not intentional. It was entirely due to their own enterprise.

The foraging of one put me off gardening at an early age. Not happy with the idea of helping Dad in the farm garden, help he could have done with, I established my own, in pioneer style, in a corner of the house croft. It involved fencing off a small area, in true homesteader fashion, reclaiming it, and sowing seeds. They were naturally radish and lettuce for quick results, growing under wire potato baskets to keep birds and hens off.

They did that all right, but had no effect on a wandering sow. She tore up the flimsy netting, howked up the baskets, ate the crop, rooted up the posts and wandered off before I could shoot her. I was devastated.

'Never mind,' Dad said. 'You can help me. Pigs do things like that.'

Some weeks later the same sow, a discontented animal broke into the byre. In one corner was stored a small marquee-type tent and poles. She ate most of the canvas. There was also half a bag of mushroom seed, part of a 'make money from your spare sheds' scheme. She ate that, helped by several frisky piglets. There was a bucket of feeding for the cow. They ate that, and chewed the bucket.

She had returned to the tent, like a glutton, when Dad walked in, attracted by the satisfied grunts. She looked up, shreds of tent hanging from her mouth. He took in the devastation, with a glance of long experience, and acted promptly. He hit her very hard on top of the head with the nearest thing handy, which happened to be a five foot long, solid metal, crowbar. Her eyes crossed, her legs buckled and she went down twitching.

'I thought I'd killed her,' he said later. But pigs have hard heads. She had recovered and we were driving her, at great speed, with her brood, to the furthest paddock.

'Never mind,' I said, admittedly without thinking. 'Pigs do things like that.'

He looked at me. I walked a little faster, and a little further away.

One good thing came out of it. The sow and piglets spread mushroom seed liberally over the whole paddock,

no surprise given the excretory habits of the pig. Prime mushrooms grew there for years. I liked mushrooms, but never forgave the destruction of my first garden.

Baby

'Don't come in here.'

'What?' I started to push open the back door of the cottage anyway.

Dad's voice came more loudly.

'Don't come in here. Go and phone the hospital.'

'What?'

I could hear another man's voice, slightly deeper, and then a woman's voice which sounded like Mrs Wilson. I kept the door ajar and stuck an ear, as far as I dared, towards the voices.

'You'll have to push harder,' Dad was saying.

'I'm not going to. I've pushed hard enough already.'

'Oh, god,' sounded like Johnny Wilson.

'Dad! What is it, Dad?'

I felt that I got the benefit of what he would like to have said to Mrs Wilson.

'Are you still here? Will you do what you're told! Go and phone the hospital. Now!'

'But Dad . . .'

'Now!'

I went. I ran up the garden path at the cottage, across the yard, and into the house. There were four of us at the village school at the time and we had sauntered home up the lonnen, as usual, confident in numbers about braving Mrs Ambler's black dog at the railway crossing. It hadn't been there today, so we had shouted at the closed door for a minute or two in the certain knowledge that it wouldn't come out, to bark and slaver behind the fence.

Then up the lonnen, spending a few minutes round the rabbit-holed elms, wearily up the last hill, and into the house. To find it empty, which was unusual. I left the three younger ones at base, rooting about for food, and set out to look for grown-ups. When I found no one in, or around the steading I tried the cottage. That was when I got the order to stay out, and phone.

The other three were busy spooning Kool-ooz powder into tumblers of water, and spreading bread, and them-selves, with jam.

'Where's Mummy?'

'Where's Daddy?'

'What's wrong?'

'I don't know. Mrs Wilson's stuck, I think. Dad's telling her to push harder. Or maybe Johnny's stuck.'

'Where's she stuck about?'

'How's she stuck?'

'What's Daddy doing there?'

'I don't know. But I've got to phone the hospital.'

Importantly, I went through the passage to the heavy, black phone which sat on the windowsill. I picked it up, tentatively. Some of the others had experimented by whispering down it, but it was the first time I'd used it.

'Send the hospital,' I whispered.

'This is the operator, 'I heard a voice saying, faintly.

'Send the hospital,' I said, more loudly.

The voice came more faintly. I listened attentively.

'You're speaking into the wrong end,' it said.

Hastily, I turned the phone round and said, for the third time: 'Send the hospital.'

'What do you mean? An ambulance? A doctor?'

'I was told to phone for the hospital.'

'What? Are you sure you're not being silly? Is that Coldstream 132 – we've had trouble with you before.'

'No, no,' I said, anxiously. 'My dad told me to phone. We need the hospital.'

'Why?' came the sharp retort.

'I don't know,' I said, lamely.

'Well, find out. And if it's important, phone again. Or, better still, get your father or mother to phone.'

'But . . .' But she had gone.

I was deeply hurt. I put the phone down and walked, crestfallen, back to the kitchen. The glasses of Kool-ooz were being refilled, the yellow crystals dissolving muddily in the water. The tin of broken wholemeal biscuits was being rifled. It wasn't often we got the run of the kitchen.

'Did you phone?', through a mouthful of biscuit.

'Yes,' I snarled, and ran back to the cottage.

I hammered on the door, and Dad answered. His sleeves were rolled up and there was what looked like blood on his hands.

'They want to know what for,' I burst out.

'Who?'

'The lady on the phone.'

'Blast her! She knows perfectly well what for. Your mother phoned to warn them, before she had to take Ailsa to the opticians. Go back and tell them Mrs Wilson's baby is half way here, and won't come any further. If they don't get an ambulance or a doctor here in five minutes, I'll be across to see them. Run!'

I ran.

'Yes?' came the same voice.

'It's Coldstream 132. Mrs Wilson's baby's half way here and not coming any further. If you don't get a doctor or an ambulance here in five minutes, my Dad's coming across to see you.'

'Right,' said the voice. 'Why didn't you say so earlier. I'll pass the message on straight away.'

Satisfied, I walked back through to the kitchen as Mum

drove up. She unloaded children as I explained what was happening. She went straight through to the phone and had a brief, pointed conversation, walked back past us and across to the cottage. There were now seven of us eating free-range, and unsupervised, while activity whirled round the cottage, and up and down the road.

A few minutes later Dad walked in, his hands clean and smelling of soap. We'd just got the lid back on the biscuit tin in time. He put the kettle on the ever-ready cooker, and spooned tea into the pot.

'Is she all right?'

Seven pairs of eyes turned towards him, while seven mouths framed with chocolate and crumbs asked the question, or at least showed willing.

'Yes, she's fine,' he said. 'She's had a baby – a little boy.'

That was all right then. Question answered. We turned back to the drinks.

'What on earth's that you're drinking?'

'Kool-ooz. It's good. Do you want some?'

'I do not. Your mother'll be across soon and you'll get your tea. A pity she got held up or none of this would have happened.'

'None of what?'

'This baby business . . . oh, it doesn't matter.'

He poured tea into the pot.

'I had a fair idea what to do. But I'd sooner have a lambing. Any time.'

Early Years

I never liked the outside toilet. I was never reassured by Dad's comment:

'Better men than us have had to use a bucket.'

There was a vulnerability, and an amount of unwanted exposure, about it that I never got used to. Going at all was a thought, when the wind was howling, or rain falling. Frost and draught were also factors to consider. I was pleased that one of the first improvements to the house, when a start was finally made, was a toilet and bathroom.

Not that the new bathroom, thanks to the penny-pinching wisdom of the trustees, was an enormous improvement. It was a converted pantry, down three steps. This was not ideal for anyone in a hurry and with eight of us, soon to be nine, someone usually was. It was rare to go without an appeal from the other side of the door, ranging from polite enquiry to frenzied hammering.

Plaster fell off the damp stone walls, rising in pale, pink distempered blisters which popped, and fell into the bath. On bath nights records were set for sprinting from the bathroom to the kitchen Aga, with instructions to 'run, like a wee hare.' The casualty rate, at the sharp left hand corner of the linoleum-covered passage, was high.

The water supply to the bathroom, like everywhere else, was a bugbear and stayed that way. When the wind blew, the wind pump spun like crazy, and the recently-installed storage tanks in the granary roof overflowed. This usually happened at night, when all the world was dark and silent, except for several gallons a minute rattling down corrugated iron into the cattle shed.

When the tanks were empty, and the demand was for water for cattle troughs, a flushing toilet and baths, the wind wouldn't blow. At the worst of times water was carried in buckets from the emergency supply, the sunken troughs half way down the farm road. With the fragments of green weed sieved out, it made excellent drinking water.

At another stage in the proceedings, when we had water and nothing to heat it with, Uncle Dave improvised with a war-time Air Force trick. He poured petrol onto sand, lit it, and to considerable excitement among the masses, boiled water in the yard. The weather was warm and we had open-air baths in the big wooden barrel used at pig killings.

It was never going to be an ideal house, but took shape as a home. Bedrooms were allocated, and bunk beds installed. The advantage of being on the top bunk was the traditional one for high ground – a good view of enemy forces. The disadvantage was falling out, or being bounced up and down by the one below. This was done, quite simply, by lying flat on the bottom bunk, putting your feet against the top mattress and pistoning legs up and down.

The disadvantage of being on the bottom was to sit up too quickly and scalp yourself on the chain-spring, mattress-support above.

The end bedroom retained a damp chill, whatever was done with it, and remained unpopular during all the personnel permutations. That front room, where the two of us had lived for the first few months, became the sitting room, rarely used except at Christmas. The focus of the house was the kitchen. It, and the living room next door, was also the warmest.

In that living room, the small window in a thick wall was replaced by French windows, double-glass doors which opened out onto a rejuvenated garden.

Electricity replaced gas lighting. I missed the comforting hiss of the gas at first. It had guided me through a lot of early reading, and long dark nights. But I quickly got used to the equally comforting thud-thud-thud of the diesel generator.

I liked the slow start, as the generator gradually built up rhythm and power. The ceiling light would go from dim, to bright glow. The process worked in reverse if Dad forgot to refuel, fading lights being accompanied by groans, or howls of fright, depending on inclination and situation at the time.

Almost as remarkable as the generator, electric light, and washing machine, was the telephone. This was largely due to the continual badgering of the post office by Tommy Carr, the haulier. He couldn't understand how a business could work effectively without a phone. He told the local manager this so often that eventually we got a party line. The other party, and the operator, complained mildly for a few weeks about small voices whispering down the line, but the novelty wore off and the small voices disappeared.

Food played an important part in our lives. The house

never seemed overcrowded, clothes never seemed important, because we were well fed.

Dad was self sufficient long before it became fashionable. This was partly because he'd been brought up that way, as one of a family of eight, largely from necessity, and partly because he enjoyed it. He had a capacity to potter, and find small jobs to do, which was remarkable. The self-sufficiency side of his farming gave him full rein to do this.

We had milk, cream and butter from the house cow. She was always milked at some time during the day, if not always twice, and seldom at regular intervals. She seemed to cope with this system, staying in milk for months at a time beyond a normal lactation.

We had milk and cream regularly, butter when he had time to make it. To do this cream was beaten in a small, wooden, hand-spun churn. The semi-butter was them pummelled, unmercifully, back and forwards along a shallow, trough-like board, squeezing the water out. From there, it was beaten and patted into shape with ridged wooden paddles, like rectangular table-tennis bats.

Cream went on the morning porridge, butter on almost everything else.

We had home-cured bacon, thick, fat-rimmed slices fried in their own grease. Pig-killing day, and one or two afterwards, were feast days of liver, spare-ribs, sausages and black puddings.

With so many children, meals were a filling-up process. Home grown potatoes and turnips, mince and dumplings, rice puddings, semolina puddings with home-made jam, sago puddings, bread and butter puddings. At night, bread and butter, bread and jam with warm milk poured over it or, a special treat with queues forming at the cooker, bread fingers dipped in egg and fried.

Eggs were a staple of the diet. We had free range hens in sheds on grass fields, and free range hens round the steading. The housed ones laid eggs in nest boxes, which stayed clean, and could be conveniently collected. They were the ones we washed and packed in 30-dozen crates for the packing station.

The hens round the steading laid eggs in unlikely crannies, and tried to hatch them if undetected. They were the ones we ate, when and if we found them.

For one penny a dozen, we ferreted them out, fighting off offended hens if necessary. Apart from nests which had a clocking hen in residence, we developed a keen sense for eggs which had been laid, and hidden, too long. Even the hen that laid them had forgotten. There was no penny a dozen for rotten ones. But the satisfaction of hurling them at walls, or pigs, was almost compensation.

We had scrambled eggs, boiled eggs, fried eggs, buttered eggs and Dad's speciality – omelette. This wasn't a lightweight, frothy effort. His omelette was made with eggs and flour, and was cooked in the heavy metal frying pan which measured eighteen inches across. An omelette like that left no one shouting for more.

At Easter, Mum would boil a panful of eggs for hours after wrapping them in onion skins, small flowers, and rags. They came out, beautifully brown and mottled, sometimes with a perfect imprint of a flower. We rolled them, smashed them, and stuffed down the dry yolks with bread and butter on Easter Monday.

We were a crowd on our own, and stuck together in the early years. Our pastimes were as self-sufficient as our food and surroundings.

After seeing stunt riders on motorbikes at Kelso show, we drove through pyramids of five-gallon drums for days. We rebuilt the six-drum pyramid, laboriously, each time after charging through on tricycles, wearing an old army helmet. No one was killed. No one was even seriously injured.

We built a brick fort in one corner of the yard, using old bricks from a knocked-out doorway and cement left behind by builders. In it, we cooked potatoes, carrots and a bit of meat in an old pan and called it Irish stew.

We tormented small livestock. With the calves, we called it rodeo. The smallest ones we would wrestle to the ground. We tried to ride the slightly bigger ones, luckily escaping decapitation when the frightened little beasts charged under the low, arched doorways of the cattle courts.

We climbed roofs. It was possible to make the full circuit from one end of the middle cattle court, via calf pens, granary, byre that used to be straw barn, washhouse and kitchen, to the far end of the house. There were two risks. One, that of falling off the steeply-pitched granary roof. The second, Dad seeing us do it.

We parachuted from the middle-court roof, using extended paper bags, landing with a thump on the dry-strawed muck of summer. We played Tarzan, Tom Mix, Rob Roy and Davy Crockett. We played football, rounders, cricket and tennis.

We got involved in many farm jobs, sometimes usefully, more often getting under the feet of the changing staff. Jake left, John arrived at a May flitting. Brian came, worked for a year or two, and left to join the RAF. Various Irishmen, with Barney as a regular, came and went at busy times, living in the bothy next to the byre, on potatoes, tea, bread and butter. Little Geordie finally left his converted bus, in a corner of the steading, and went back to Newcastle. Some time before he went, he summed up what it was like for adults who came in contact with us. We had a child-minder, for what must have been a rare night out for Mum and Dad. Geordie, collecting his pint of milk, told the bemused woman sympathetically:

'Hinny, you'll need eyes in your arse to watch this lot.'

The farm changed around us. Not perceptibly, day by day, as we walked to school and dawdled back, or fought and played at nights, weekends and holidays. But when I thought back, to the beginning, I could see the differences.

We had better crops. There was a new shed and new sheep pens. Old buildings were in slightly better repair. Livestock stayed where they were put – for a lot of the time. There was more machinery and Dad's enthusiasm and energy to keep things moving along. The estate, where the late, unlamented – by us – Captain had been replaced by his son, the Colonel, put up some new fencing despite facing an uphill financial struggle.

I couldn't put a finger on all the changes. But one morning I woke up and found we had been there four years.

Lambing

We believed that the farm stood on the site of an old monastery, and that it was slightly haunted. Our belief was based on the filled in, pointed, window of the small, stone shed where the diesel generator now, prosaically, stood; a remark about Carmelite monks by the Colonel; a creepy feeling about the damp end bedroom; a reported sighting of a monk at the end of a bed, and the way odd socks disappeared from the bulging sock drawer.

There were two schools of thought about the socks. One argued that it must be a ghost, because who else would take single socks. The other school argued that surely there weren't many one-legged ghostly monks going about, particularly in search of child's size 13 socks?

The believers were in the majority. When various items of girls' wear disappeared, rather than believe we had a transvestite ghost on our hands, we invented a partner for him. Willie and Matilda became part of the household, responsible for most lost items, spillages, breakages, and disappearances. They were a quiet pair, and didn't interfere much otherwise, probably finding it difficult to get a word in to a household where long silences were not so much unusual as unknown. They were more terrified by what we might do to them, than what they might do to us.

That was why it came as a shock to see Willie walking slowly along the yard, in the grey half light of a March morning, as rain teemed down. We stood, silent for once, at the kitchen window, until we saw that the hooded monk was wearing an oilskin coat and leggings, carrying a crook in one hand and with a sopping lamb under the other arm. Dad was in the middle of lambing.

His hood was a hessian potato sack, with the top corners tucked in to sit comfortably on his cap and across his shoulders. He threw it off at the back door, passing the lamb in before taking off jacket and leggings. We put the lamb, with the speed of long practice, onto a sheet of newspaper in the bottom, cooler, oven of the Aga and half closed the door. Mum poured him a cup of coffee from the percolator, which sat on permanent standby on the cooker during lambing.

His other reviver was a mixture of egg, milk, sugar and a dash of rum, whipped together. That morning he settled for cowboy coffee, boiled black, hot off the range.

Between sips, he rubbed Snowfire into his chapped hands, a thick, green ointment which temporarily sealed the splits in the skin caused by continual soaking and drying in rain and afterbirth.

'Have many lambed during the night?'

'Not bad. Six. A three, three pairs, and two singles. One

of the singles isn't up to much.'

'Why?'

'He won't suck. I gave him a good rub down with some straw, stood him up, and he sucked away for a minute or

two. Then he fell over and I discovered he'd been sucking a bit of wool. He'd got off the tit all together.'

He didn't seem to think this was as funny as we did.

'It's nothing to laugh at. Donnert little thing. But I think he'll make it all right.'

'Are you going to put one off the three onto her?'

'No, I don't think so. The three's doing well. She's a good ewe, that. The one with a notch at the top of her left lug?'

I nodded, as if I knew.

'We thought you were Willie coming along the yard with that hood thing on.'

'Willie? Willie who?'

'You know – Willie. Willie and Matilda.'

At that time, in that weather, ready for the breakfast which was about to appear in front of him, he wasn't impressed.

'Oh, that. Piece of nonsense.'

He started on the bacon and eggs, adding: 'He'd have more sense than going out in that weather anyway. Only shepherds go out in that.'

He ate quietly, checking the market reports in the previous day's *Journal,* finished the tea which had replaced the coffee, pushed the plate away, and stood up. He checked the lamb in the oven, which was showing signs of revival.

'I'll get him back with his mother in an hour or two. Can you keep an eye on him?'

He looked out of the window. There was the faint possibility of a break in the clouds, but it didn't look inviting. He wasn't issuing invitations.

'Right. Get some wellingtons and coats on. I'm going to have to move some ewes. We're stowed out in the pens.'

'But it's still raining.'

'You won't melt. I'd get Jack, but he's busy putting the grain drill spouts and cogs on – for when it dries up. Come on, it won't take long.'

If I had a shilling, I thought, for every time I'd heard that. When we went out, the rain had eased off to a drizzle and a weak sun was trying to break through.

'Where are we taking them?'

'The Big Hill. I've got plenty of bales out there to give them some shelter.'

After lambing, each ewe was put in an individual pen with her lambs, to 'mother up'. Most of them did, but not all. One was haltered to a corner of the pen, with two small lambs huddled at the other side.

'Are you twinning them on?'

'No. They're her own. But the thrawn bitch won't take them.'

'What'll you do?'

'Probably break her neck. No, I'll try for another day or two. She might take them yet. We'll see if we can give them a suck just now.'

He straddled the wooden hurdle, which formed the front of the pen, taking the weight on his hands as one of the rails cracked.

'I'll have to make some new ones. I'll do myself an injury one of these days.'

He pushed the ewe further into the corner with his hip, pulling the two lambs towards him and fitting one onto a teat. The ewe tossed her head and stamped her feet, trying to kick the lamb. He persevered for several minutes, kneeling down to make sure the lamb was securely on the teat, forcing the ewe to stand still. Then he did the same with the second one, watching with satisfaction as the little tail waved eagerly, up and down, as the lamb sucked. He felt the small, rounded belly, which had filled up surprisingly well.

'That'll keep them going an hour or two. We'll leave you tied up all the same.'

He climbed out again, gingerly, in case of accidents, and began to select the ewes with stronger lambs which were to move from the small paddocks round the lambing shed out to the Big Hill.

The ewes still to lamb, more than 150, were turned out onto the main lambing field. After being fed with a mixture of oats and sugar beet pulp, they waddled off to graze what grass there was and nibble turnips which had been laid out for them.

We set off towards the gate, at the other end of the straw-bale lambing pens, with eleven ewes and eighteen lambs trying to go in twenty nine different directions.

Dad caught a bouncy little lamb by the leg with his crook, and picked it up. It had an orange ball of dung trapped under its tail.

'What's wrong with it?'

'Nothing. Getting too well fed, that's all.'

He eased the ball away with his fingers and set the lamb down again, to where the mother was turning in circles.

'You'll go better now, little 'un.'

Moving ewes, and lambs a few days old, wasn't easy. Two ewes, scenting welcome change, set off at a gallop, ignoring their lambs. Another insisted on trying to get back to the gate we had left, looking for a lamb which was behind her. The others milled about, making the classical sheep's progress of three runs forward and two runs back.

The lambs couldn't be hurried. They had to find their own pace, which was slow. Any attempt to push them on only caused them to turn in circles. A gentle prod with foot or stick made them tumble into the nearest puddle, or bog down in the mud. At least a watery sun was now shining and the drizzle had stopped.

Lambing

We moved them on, a continual process of nudging, guiding, suggesting and coaxing, until we reached the gate at the top of the Big Hill, so called because of steepness rather than extent. It was fourteen acres of permanent grass.

When the last one was through, we shut the gate. Queen held the ewes back for a few minutes until the lambs sorted themselves out by blaring, and the ewes decided by smell. The two front runners spun repeatedly, stamping their front feet at the dog and trampling unwary lambs with their back ones. From the top of the hill, we could see the Cheviots clearing in the distance, and, in the other direction, wisps of morning smoke rising from Coldstream.

We watched them trot off across the wet grass. He leant on the crook, and pushed his cap back from his brow with one hand.

'That's a grand lot of lambs. That's one of the best bits about lambing. Watching them run off like that.'

'I didn't know there were any good bits.'

'Don't be so miserable.'

'Well, what about that one in the Aga. And those two that couldn't suck. And we had two dead ones yesterday.'

'Everybody has a few dead ones. That's nature. It can't be helped.'

'We don't need to keep sheep.'

He was astonished.'

'A farm needs sheep. And cattle. You can't just grow barley, barley, barley.'

'It's less trouble.'

'And not very good farming.'

'What about the way they keep getting out?'

'Not very often. We're getting the fences done as fast as we can afford it.'

We were almost back at the lambing field. A seagull sucking in cleanings, the afterbirth, had reached the stage of wondering whether it had made a mistake. It didn't know whether to keep sucking, or try to regurgitate. Queen chased it, and it flew away, too bunged up to shriek.

'Dirty brutes. As bad as crows.'

He strode round the field, on the alert for a ewe which might have started lambing since our last visit. We found one, on her own as expected, and trying to lamb into a puddle, which was what I expected.

He eased her round, talking to her coaxingly as he eased the lamb out.

'It's got its head lying on its front feet,' I said, excitedly.

For the first time that morning, he looked weary.

'That,' he said, 'is the way it's supposed to come out. When it isn't coming that way, you worry.'

He felt around gently, and eased a second lamb out. We cleared their mouths of mucous, and held the ewe until she had recognised them and started to lick, apprehensively at first, then with more life.

'You've got to be careful about that. I've seen me lamb one in the middle of the field, let her up, and she's off towards Berwick at fifty miles an hour. Never looking back. It plays hell with the dog.'

'This one seems settled enough.'

'Right. Pick the lambs up, and take them back to a pen. She'll follow. I'll take a walk round the far hedge.'

I set off, one licked, but still damp, lamb in each hand, the ewe nuzzling and following behind. She was a good follower. There was no hesitation as I walked steadily on. She kept her nose glued to them, giving deep-throated blares to answer their plaintive bleats. Back at the pens, I opened one up, laid the lambs on fresh straw and shut her in when she followed. Another job well done.

I wiped my hands down my trousers and waited. Not for long. The dog was bringing all the ewes back in, Dad close behind. Once into the pens, he headed for a ewe, caught her leg with the crook, and whipped her onto her side.

'Besom,' he puffed. 'Hanging it. Couldn't get close enough to catch her. Going like a racehorse.'

The lamb hadn't been hung for long, but the head which had come out in advance of the legs, then jammed at the shoulders, was already beginning to swell. It had to be pushed back in, and the front feet brought into the proper position. With the aid of some lambing oil lubricant, firm persuasion, and a little cursing, he got the head back in. After some more guddling about, he got the legs into position. He fastened a piece of twine round the slippery front feet, and pulled steadily, downwards, while I held the ewe's head.

'A muckle single,' he growled. 'Look at the size of that. No wonder it jammed. Come on – breathe.'

The lamb showed no signs of doing any such thing. He slapped it, gently at first, along the ribs, then harder.

'Get some straw. Rub it. Hard.'

I rubbed. He grabbed another piece of straw himself, and positively scrubbed the lamb. There was a brief lift of rib cage.

'That's it. Go on. We're winning.'

I rubbed savagely, but the rib cage didn't lift again. It was starting to drizzle.

He stuck a piece of straw up the lamb's nose. That seemed to work. It sneezed, sucked, and started to breathe. As we sat back on our heels to relax, the breathing stopped again. One or two slaps didn't help. He leapt to his feet, took it by the back legs, and began to swing it from side to side. Up and down it went, like a soggy, woolly, pendulum. It began to breathe when he laid it down. Then it stopped. We looked at each other. I was going to say 'Another good thing about lambing,' but thought better of it.

We made a final assault, rubbing and massaging as hard as we could without crushing it. The breathing started again, and mine stopped, as we looked hopefully at the small body. The breathing continued. The lamb jerked and stretched. Dad brought the ewe's head round towards it and, with some persuasion, she began to lick. The lamb jerked again, and tried to sit up.

We stood up, rain dripping off us.

'All in a day's work. Let's get them into a pen where it's dry. Do you still think there's more bad things than good things about lambing?'

It seemed a pity to spoil the moment. I picked up the lamb, and didn't answer.

Boar

We started a pig herd with four Large White sows and a Large White boar, with the emphasis on large. He was four yards long with teeth like an alligator, including tusks. His skin was thick and scaly, covered with bristly hair, and he slavered a lot.

To me, he was enormous. To my visiting Uncle Laurie, he was simply big. Like every other visitor he was roped in to do a job. We were hinting to the boar, rather than telling him, where we would like him to go. He was digging up the yard, like an amiable rhinoceros, while making up his mind.

Laurie, safely behind a guiding board, spoke to Dad, who held a fork.

'How heavy is he, anyway?'

'About 700 lbs or so,' said Dad. 'I think. We've not weighed him for a while.'

'Since when?'

'Since he was about six months old!'

Laurie studied the boar as we moved a little closer. The boar raised his head, perked his ears, and chopped his tusks together once or twice. We stepped back to our original positions, like slow motion country dancers.

'Where does he live?' Laurie asked.

Dad grinned, flicking the cigarette from one side of his mouth to the other.

'Anywhere he likes,' he answered. 'Go on, man. We haven't got all day.'

The boar grunted, half warning, half pleasure, as Dad rubbed the prongs of the fork along his scaly hide.

'Come on. Into there.'

There was a brief pause as Dad pushed gently with the two-pronged fork, and the boar pushed firmly back. It was touch and go, but the boar went. We shut the door of the pen behind him and Laurie sighed with relief.

'It's all right,' Dad said. 'He's a lot quieter these days since he got back from Marldown the last time.'

'That's the next door farm?'

'Aye, Peter Wight's. When was it? About a month ago.'

'It was when we were on holiday from school.'

'About a month. He's a free-range boar, you know. He'd got across to Marldown somehow, probably lifted a gate off its hinges or something. Well, Peter's got a big boar too.'

'They found each other, I take it?'

'That's one way of putting it. They nearly killed each other.'

'Did anybody try and stop them?'

'Did they hell! Peter phoned me up. He said there's two boars out here trying to kill each other. Could I go and stop them.'

Laurie laughed.

'So you said you'd be right over?'

'I said, Peter, if yours gets killed I'll pay for it. If mine gets killed I'll come over and pick up what's left.'

'Did he like that?'

'He didn't say anything for a few seconds. I thought he'd put the phone down, but I could hear squeals in the background.'

'Peter?'

'No, no, the boars. Then Peter came on again. He said, "I've just had another look out of the window. I think you're right. I'll phone you back when one of them's dead." '

'So his died?'

'No, they both lived. I didn't even have to go and get him. Peter phoned up to say he'd left Marldown and was last seen heading home. We went straight out to look for him, but no sign. He'd disappeared. We found him three days later.'

'He was in the hayshed.'

I could feel the panic yet. We had crept into the old, tiled hayshed through the small door, on an army-game raid. Angus stepped onto a heap of loose hay and straw, which, after a second or two, began to rise into the air. His mouth opened and his eyes began to bulge, probably as much as mine, as we stared at each other. As he flung himself off and headed for the door, a poor second to me, the snorting and grunting from behind told us what was under the straw.

We peered cautiously round the corner. The boar had levered himself into a sitting position, head and massive shoulders sticking out of the nest of straw he'd made for himself. He was covered in cuts, scratches and dried blood, still too weary to get onto all four feet. We didn't try to tempt him. At least we knew where he was.

Dad kept an eye on him, once we had told our story, and a day later the boar finally tottered out into the daylight. He made it to a water trough and drank for several minutes, then started rooting about, listlessly at first, but with more animation as he picked up small items of animal, vegetable and mineral. Dad coaxed him into a pen with a few pounds of meal, and within a week he was his usual cocky self, knocking the wooden door off to prove it.

'Why do you keep him,' Laurie asked, as we walked up the yard, 'when he seems to cause as much trouble?'

'He leaves good pigs,' Dad said simply. 'He's a good boar and he's not really vicious. Just a bit awkward when he feels like it.'

Angus agreed with that more than anyone. It was the second time the boar had threatened to cut him short. The first time was when four of us ran away from home one wet and windy night, a reply to brutal parental oppression, which had consisted of being sent to bed early.

Our supplies consisted of apples, and a bag of broken chocolate wholemeal biscuits, taken from the square tin which always sat in the kitchen cupboard. Three of us made it in the dusk as far as the round corn bin, which sat in the corner of the Windmill Field. It stood about four feet high, with a lid held in place by a metal pin, and was half-full of sheep feeding.

We made it in some haste from the gate, across the thirty yards or so of wet grass, to the bin. The one who didn't make it was Angus. The reason for all the activity was the boar.

He loomed out of the dusk as we were half way. Showing initiative, I bolted forward, holding one of the girls by the hand and shouting at the other. Feverishly, I pulled the pin out of the lid and hauled it off, pushing the girls in headfirst and scrambling up frantically myself.

This wasn't easy. The bin was made of corrugated, circular metal which was slippy in the rain.

I could feel the boar's hot breath on my bare legs. The tusks were within inches of tearing into me, as my feet slithered and slipped on the metal, and my fingers gripped desperately for the top of the bin. With a final, frantic pull I went over the edge and fell on top of the girls. I looked out over the parapet and saw that the boar was nowhere near me, and never had been. He was eyeing up Angus, who had made the mistake of changing his mind half-way.

'Run,' we bawled, three faces in a row peering over the edge.

After being hard on our heels, with a clear run to the bin, he had decided to turn back. Doing that, he lost his footing and went down briefly on one knee. He got up quickly, but the boar by then was much closer, ready to investigate, and Angus' options had become severely limited.

'Run!', we howled again, standing up and flinging handfuls of feeding, apples, and bits of broken biscuit in the general direction of the boar.

All he could do now was run for the gate. He did it in good style. Head down, arms pumping, little legs plunging up and down in over-size wellingtons through the mud, he really could feel the boar's hot breath.

'Run,' we yelled for a completely superfluous third time. He couldn't have run any faster, but the boar seemed to be gaining.

'He wouldn't have hurt you,' Dad said later, but that wasn't the impression we got at the time, particularly

Angus.

'He'd've killed me,' he said, in an aggrieved voice, and we agreed with him. Luckily, the argument was only theoretical by then.

With a final sizzling burst, Angus reached the gate and scrambled up the wooden spars like a monkey, falling over the other side. Picking himself up, he didn't hesitate. He kept going, at a rate of knots, steadily disappearing into the darkness while the boar grunted and chopped his tusks at the gate.

After giving it two or three dunts with his head and shoulders, he wandered off up the hedge. After some time we picked what sheep feeding we could out of our hair and clothes, slid down the bin, tiptoed across to the gate, and followed the path Angus had travelled, at greater speed, some time before.

Once it had been established that all four of us were still sound in wind and limb, Dad was annoyed that we had agitated the boar and, worse, left the lid off the feed bin when it was raining. Mum was annoyed that we had gone out at all. We were grateful to be back, and quietly went to bed.

I mentioned some of this to Uncle Laurie. He turned to Dad.

'Are you sure it wouldn't have touched them?'

'Fairly sure. He's not the quietest pig I've ever had, but he's never actually attacked anybody. And he does leave good pigs – look at this.'

He opened the door of the semi-dark, dusty shed we kept fattening pigs in. I stood on tiptoe to look into the gloom at a pen of a dozen or so, round, chunky, pigs which looked up and oinked expectantly.

Dad scooped up a bucket of meal and tipped it over into their trough. They pushed in, grunting and giving small squeals, till they were settled into their regular eating positions. Or almost. One or two insisted on looking along the trough, seeing an imaginary ingredient that a friend was getting that they weren't, and changing places by barging in.

We stood in silence. It's possible to watch pigs eating for minutes on end without getting bored. They change places, and move about, like a small swarm of bees.

'Look at the hams on them,' Dad said proudly. 'Grand pigs. You can't change a boar like that just because he eats children.'

He grinned at Laurie, and flicked the cigarette across to the other side. I hoped he was joking.

The Vicar

'Come back!'
'Aw, Mum!'
'Come back. Sit down. Eat your tea.'

'But Mum . . . he's in the yard.'

'Be quiet. And don't move. Be polite.'

The vicar's visits were not appreciated. Katrine had brought the news to the tea table that he was on his way and several of us jammed the doorway trying to get out. Until my mother ordered us to our seats and we trooped moodily back.

She went to the door to greet our visitor. There was silence round the big table.

'Dad, can we . . .'

'No,' he said, from his carver chair at the head of the table, his back to the massive wooden sideboard. He didn't say it happily, but buttered a scone and chewed thought-

The Vicar

fully. The vicar's High Church of England approach tested his Presbyterian upbringing and native politeness to the limit.

We half-stood, muttering and nudging each other, until the vicar sat down. He'd forgotten to take his bicycle clips off again.

He was an old man. Not as old, by many years, as we judged him to be, watching him cut a scone carefully into triangles, but old enough.

He dressed in full black, with a dog collar. The black was shabby and faded. His boots were sturdy, but old, scuffed from the walk up our road and a hundred others, the trouser bottoms spattered with spots of mud and flecks of oil from the bike chain.

He wore round, gold-rimmed spectacles and the last thing he did before entering the room was to remove his round-brimmed, flat topped black hat.

He ate fastidiously and completely killed the buzz of conversation which always went with a mealtime at that table. My mother worked valiantly to get it going again. Dad offered him the cheese, a muscular red cheddar that he favoured.

The vicar looked over the top of his round spectacles and pursed his mouth.

'No thank you. Only fit for mousetraps I always think.'

Dad pointedly cut off about quarter of a pound and ate it with wedges of thick soda scone. Conversation became restricted to mother and the vicar.

Until then it had been a normal tea time for us, a steady demolition of piled plates accompanied by small hands reaching as far as they could, one or two cups knocked over, a wish for longer arms and a regular chorus of 'Pass the . . .'

On the table there were three types of scone – currant, treacle and plain, the plain type an inch thick and rising. There were also what we called pancakes and Dad called drop-scones, made from spoonfuls of thick yellow batter dropped onto the girdle which sat on the Aga cooker hotplate.

There were two plates of sliced bread, honey, home made jam and home made butter.

The butter was soft and yellow, made from thick cream skimmed off the Jersey house-cow's milk. We loved to spread it thickly enough to show the teethmarks as we bit down through it to the bread or scone below. When the cow occasionally dried off and we had to resort to bought butter, the taste was never the same, or had the soft, golden consistency of summer.

Winter butter was different, sometimes dramatically. Billy, the cow, full name William Buttercup after the whim of one small child, stayed in the byre during the winter months and the change of diet affected her output.

Butter became much paler, which was bearable. But too many turnips were disastrous. The smell and flavour came through and tainted the milk and butter. Dad, who refused to believe that cream was sour until it grew whiskers, and dismissed any taint short of sheep-dip as imagination, continued to eat turnip-flavoured butter. The rest of us worked hard at increasing Billy's hay intake and hoped for an early spring.

There were two jams on the table. Rhubarb, which had set firm and solid, and strawberry which needed careful application with a paintbrush. It came from one of the less successful days in the kitchen.

Our jam-making sessions varied. They could be serious, thorough affairs with ingredients weighed carefully, boiling times adhered to and any additives carefully measured. These were usually the least successful.

The best results, as with her cooking, came when Mum was doing several things at once. When cooking, she threw in a handful of this, a pinch of that and half a bag of something else. When jam-making she tipped whatever fruit had been gathered into the pan, guessed the sugar to within a pound or two and boiled and simmered it until she remembered to take it off.

We liked to take an active part in this. Gooseberry and rhubarb didn't draw much of a crowd, but when strawberries were foaming and bubbling in the big pan on the cooker, competition round the setting saucer was fierce.

This was the saucer onto which jam was skimmed off at intervals, as she was passing, and set on a bench to cool. Sometimes it got the chance, at others a finger scooped it into a young mouth. Jam bubbling on the stove, sweet steam filling the kitchen, several children milling and squawking round a saucer of hot jam, sunshine beating through the window and my mother trying to keep control were the sound and smell of summer.

The jam before the vicar had been made on a quiet day when most of us were at school. Measured and boiled to the textbook, it flowed easily. The vicar gingerly spooned some of the liquid onto his bread. It soaked into the unbuttered surface, leaving a faint pink trace and half a strawberry.

It was possibly the only thing Dad and the vicar saw eye to eye on. Bread or scones were only made to carry one thing at a time, either butter or jam. Never both together. You had to make your choice. The vicar had chosen jam and looked as if he wished he hadn't.

'My own view,' he said in his clipped, precise voice, 'is that strawberry jam needs to be boiled for quarter of an hour longer than one would think.'

His other views on jam making lasted some time. My mother listened politely, but the rest of the audience became restless. Chairs were scuffled and swung onto their back legs, despite warning glances. Oblivious of the atmosphere, and used to giving sermons where the audience had no right of reply, the vicar had launched into a thorough review of the respective merits of raspberry and strawberry jams.

Dad broke the deadlock with the last of his gingerbread, layered with butter. He swallowed it, drank the dregs of his tea and stood up.

'Excuse me,' he said, 'I have some sheep to look.'

This was closely followed by a chorus of 'Please may I leave the table?' and we charged out after him. He'd never had such willing helpers, a desire which lasted as far as the yard when we checked, faded and disappeared in various directions. He smiled, called the collie, and made for open country lighting a cigarette.

A few minutes later Mum and the vicar came to the door. I studied him carefully from the coalhouse roof where three of us were lying, planning a mortar bomb attack with a Bird's Custard Powder tin full of water. Filled, and left to soak for a few minutes, those thick cardboard tins exploded most satisfactorily when they hit the ground. After a muttered exchange of views, we decided a direct hit on the vicar was not in our short-term interests. We studied him instead.

There was a sallow tinge to his skin, caused by his belief in the virtues of a cold bath every morning and a disbelief in the value of soap. The sallow face and hands, and dowdy black clothes, gave him a dingy look as he replaced his hat just outside the doorway.

I also found him as boring as it was possible for a child to find an adult. Yet there was a curious dignity about him as he stood there, and in the way he stuck to his beliefs.

They included an extremely High Church approach to his services, 'var neor Catholic' as one or two muttered, and a belief that parishioners, good Christians or not, were to be visited.

He made his rounds by ancient bicycle, calling on the lonely and making them wish he'd left them that way, calling on the sick to let them know what hell really was, calling on the miserable and making them sad.

And calling on perfectly innocent families, like ours, who had never done him any harm, much as some of us thought we would like to, fingering the custard powder tin lovingly. He did it all without, as far as we ever saw on several dozen visits, a spark of humour. But he did it because he saw it as his duty and won a grudging admiration.

We waited for the last rites of the visit. We weren't disappointed. He opened his old army haversack, a remainder and reminder of his time as a First World War chaplain, and brought them out.

'It's the same ones!', one of the three whispered in outrage.

'No, it's not,' said a second. 'They look worse.'

'They can't be,' I said, stamping my authority on the conversation as the longest-lived recipient.

We were looking at him hand over a selection of his home-grown apples, carefully collected and stored in the depths of the twelve-room vicarage, where he lived alone.

If he had handed them out at the time they were picked, or allowed us to pick them ourselves, or turned a blind eye to twilight raids on the trees, we would have looked on him more kindly.

He did none of these things. He protected them jealously, picked the trees clean, and stored the fruit away. Then he brought them out, packed them parsimoniously in his haversack and took them on his rounds.

He handed them to my mother as if they were orchids. She thanked him politely. He checked to see if his bicycle clips were in his pocket, found he still had them on, mounted the bicycle stiffly and rode away.

We came down from the roof. I picked an apple from the bowl and squeezed it thoughtfully. That skin. That colour. That texture. It hadn't changed. It was like nothing more than a yellowish sponge-rubber ball. I looked at Mum.

'I bet it would bounce.'

'Don't be silly,' she said defensively. 'It was a kind thought. Put it back in the bowl if you don't want it.'

It was hard to know. Depending on the sort of day she'd

had she might laugh. Or she might not. The other two were making encouraging noises from behind. I threw it firmly on the floor and it shot back up at an angle. I made a smart, swooping catch and grinned at her.

She laughed.

'Get out. Take them with you. Do what you like with them.'

We tested them all, individually, for bounce then bombarded the hens, using an old tennis racket, shouting 'forteigh-love,' 'deuce' and 'boil for at least quarter of an hour longer than one would think' and 'only fit for mousetraps, you know.'

'We should have lobbed the water bomb,' said one.

'He wouldn't have thought it was funny,' I said. But I wished we'd done it all the same.

Estate

It was a tense meeting. Dad was rubbing the back of his head and the Colonel was fingering his moustache. He was a sandy figure – sandy hair, sandy moustache, brown jacket and suede shoes. He spoke with a slight stutter.

'It's a b . . . b . . . bloody shame, Tommy, but there's nothing we can do for them now. The c . . . c . . . creditors are pushing too hard. They've no option, b . . . but to go.'

Dad said 'Aye,' thoughtfully, and kept rubbing.

'We can sort the d . . . details out later,' the Colonel continued. 'It's j . . . just to know how you feel about the chance of extra land.'

'Delighted.' Dad said simply. 'But it's a pity about Jean.'

'It is. I c . . . could think of one or two other t . . . tenants I'd rather have lost. It's not easy f . . . for any of us at present.'

'No, it isn't. But the extra land would help. How much exactly?'

They studied a map the Colonel produced from his jacket pocket.

'Ahuh. Right down to the station from our Croft – North Bank, Big Flat and Station Field. And those two between us and Marldown. That's, aye, about 72 acres.'

The Colonel folded the map and crumpled it back into his pocket.

'Wilson will be in t . . . touch. But I can take it you're quite happy with the p . . . prospect?'

'You can, Colonel.'

The Colonel smiled.

'Good. I'm pleased for you. I know it's not been easy. Goodbye.'

'Goodbye.'

We stood and watched him go, but he turned back briefly.

'By the way, I'm d . . . dropping the rent day ritual. Quite possible to p . . . pay by post in this day and age.'

'Fine. I'll do that.'

'Good.'

This time he went.

'What's he mean he's dropping the rent?'

'I wish he had meant that. No, he's talking about everybody turning up at the hotel to pay their rent and drinking his whisky.'

'What happens?'

'Well, I've to put a collar and tie on and go to the hotel in the village on rent day along with the other tenants on the estate. And pay the rent for the half year.'

'Is that all?'

'It's an old custom. They've got those two that work on the estate, Do-Little and Do-Less, holding ropes so that only the tenants get through. As if anybody would try to get in and pay a rent.'

'Do they?'

'Do they what?'

'Try to get in to pay a rent if they don't have to?'

'No, they're worried they try to get through at the free whisky. Some of the tenants make a big enough hole in that.'

We had walked into the granary and he was starting to shovel calf feeding into a bag. I picked a piece of shiny, brown, locust bean from the mixture and started chewing it, waiting for the sweetness to burst out.

'Here, hold this bag for me.'

I held it with both hands, keeping the mouth of the bag open so that he could shovel the mixture in more quickly.

The sweetness of the locust bean soon disappeared, and I spat the fibrous remnants out. The calves would never notice.

'But you don't drink,' I said, resuming the discussion.

'No,' he said, 'I don't get much back for my rent money, in the way of whisky.'

He put the last shovelful in, took the bag and bounced it up and down once or twice before swinging it onto his back, and headed for the door.

'But one or two of them must be recovering about ten shillings an acre in whisky by the time they get poured out, into their cars.'

He walked briskly along the yard and I trotted alongside.

'Open that door. Right.'

The pen of calves, a few months old, pushed forward towards the trough. He cuffed them away, without malice.

'Get back. Just a minute. There you are.'

We stood and watched them eating.

'Aye, some of them try to get their money's worth. No wonder he's doing away with it. Waste of time.'

'What was that about getting more fields?'

'Jean's gone bankrupt. No money. Poor soul. I'll go and see if she needs a hand with anything. Not that there's much I can do for her now. If some of those sods that owed her money had paid up she might have come out with a little bit.'

He moved forward and caught a calf which was mouthing the feeding, but not making much attempt to eat. He held its ear, to test the temperature, and put a hand on its chest.

'Bit of a heave. We'll have to keep an eye on that one.'

He let it go, and it shot backwards against the wall, before turning and running away. We went out.

With the takeover, letters from the estate's London solicitors, their London chartered surveyors, and their local solicitors, came in frequently. It became difficult to close the lid of his pigeon-hole desk.

'Everybody's got to get their snout in the trough,' he said. 'This estate must be supporting about five professional firms one way and another. It's as bad as the tenants with their whisky. Or those devils claiming that Jean owes them money.'

He got bitter about this development. Not content with refusing to pay for grazing they had had, one or two were claiming that Jean owed them for stock.

'There are some bad people about,' he said. 'If they can't make a living without cheating a poor woman, it's a bad job.'

Jean, her sisters, the former prisoners of war, the dogs,

106

and the cats, went quietly. Jean got a job milking cows at a farm near Coldstream. Her impressive collection of horse brasses was, years later, donated to the local museum. I saw her over the years, and she changed no further than that autumn morning we dehorned the cattle – the same baggy trousers, boots, cropped grey hair, cap and pipe. She seemed happy enough, but it couldn't be the same as running your own farm.

Despite feeling sorry for her, Dad blessed her at times, in the heat of the moment, as he struggled to sort out the Hotel Lands steading, the fencing and the crops. It was another 72 acres in much the same condition as the 153 we had started with four years earlier. He also had a milestone in his financial farming affairs to look forward to.

'Big business, boys,' he said, sitting at the desk, holding the tortoise-shell Parker pen, which spluttered ink. He carefully wrote out the Commercial Bank of Scotland cheque, for one thousand and forty pounds, signed it, and blotted it.

'That'll make that old bee at Haddington sit up,' he said happily, referring, I guessed, to the bank manager. I had never met this almost-mythical figure and Dad met him as seldom as possible. But I knew he wrote testy letters when something called the overdraft got too big. Dad seldom mentioned finance. I never knew how much he thought about money, but he didn't talk about it.

Farming was a question of growing crops and breeding livestock, and selling them to grow more crops and breed more livestock or, possibly, to take on more land if the chance came. It was unusual for him to make a performance of signing a cheque but, as he explained, it was the first four-figure one.

For good measure, he got to make it out twice. The first one was made payable to the Trustees, of fond memory. The solicitors wrote back, politely, in a London solicitorish sort of way, and asked him to make it out to them.

With the gloss off the transaction, he wrote it out quickly one dinner time with a ball-point pen. The solicitors accepted it quite happily.

The Trustees were also anxious to increase the rent. But the Colonel, playing Father Christmas to us as he did at the annual Woman's Institute children's party every year, said no increase was necessary.

The estate also fenced some of the fields, as they had said they would do. Windows and doors were replaced or repaired at the Hotel Lands steading. A new hayshed, metal pillars and corrugated iron, was erected to replace the tumble-down wood and tile building opposite the old pond.

For some reason, it was built on precisely the same site, more than 150 yards from the main steading, such as it was. No one knew why.

'It's fine there,' was all he would say. It was all he could say, after it had been erected. I began to detect slight cracks in his infallibility.

Dad appreciated what the Colonel did but a small estate, with a legacy of debt and death duties, couldn't survive by holding down rents and making improvements. Within two years most of what was left was on the market, including us as sitting tenants.

It was finally settled, leaving us with a new landlord to deal with, and the Colonel with the big white house overlooking the river, not much more than 100 acres, and a dislike of modern business methods.

'I hope it works out all right for you, Tommy,' he said, after telling him about the completed sale. 'I'm worried that you may f . . . find them rather more awkward than us to deal with.'

'That's a pity,' Dad said. 'I've appreciated what you tried to do in the past few years.'

'M . . . money,' said the Colonel, drily. 'If my f . . . father had looked after it more carefully, we wouldn't have had the problems we've got.'

He looked rather wistful.

'P'raps I wasn't cut out for it anyway. But I'd like to have given it a b . . . b . . . better try. Mark you, I d . . .

don't care much for modern methods. Sail very close to the wind.'

'Oh?' Dad said politely.

'Oh, yes. T . . . tell you one thing and do another. Offer you one p . . . price and then change it on a t . . . technicality. Eventually I told him that we did b . . . business my way, or not at all.'

'Oh, yes?'

'I told him, quite b . . . bluntly, that after a lifetime of dealing with my father, nothing c . . . could surprise me. But, I said, you're the only man I've ever met who was a bigger b . . . bloody liar than my father.'

'Ah.'

'But good luck.'

'Thanks,' Dad said. 'And thank you.'

They shook hands, and the sandy Colonel drove away. We were onto our third landlord in six years.

Tattoo

As our fat pigs left the farm, they were tattooed on the shoulder. This was to identify them in case of a disease outbreak and, more important, to make sure the money came to the right place. The pigs didn't know this and took a dim view of tattooing. I didn't blame them as we chivvied them round the pen, trying to get them into the passage.

The tattooing stick was an arrangement of short, heavy needles set in a metal head, on a stubby wooden handle. Swung hard aginst the pig's shoulder, it left an indelible number. Hardly surprising, I thought. Forty or fifty needles puncturing the skin at one blow would leave a mark, make a pig squeal and make those still to do doubly nervous.

The lorry driver wielding the tatooing stick that morning didn't help. He was a sweating man, in a hurry to get his next load. He charged round the pen, trying to swear the pigs out into the passage.

'Steady,' Dad said. 'They're quiet pigs. Give them time.'

It was true. They were used to a leisurely life style. Lying down, standing up to eat, scratching, and lying down again. They were pigs of well over 200 lbs and could be coaxed or guided, but not bullied. That lorry driver tried to bully them.

'Look,' he said argumentatively, 'I'm running late as it is. Get on, man!' He was speaking to a passing pig and aimed a kick while doing so.

'That'll do,' Dad said firmly. 'If you're going to be like that, just wait in the lorry and we'll get them.'

I looked over. That seemed a tall order. Three of us weren't making much headway. Reducing numbers to two didn't seem the best idea. But the driver took the hint and cooled down. We kept coaxing, talking to the pigs as if they understood, and soon the first one found the open door. It inspected the gap carefully, grunted and sniffed its way out, and the rest followed. Dad followed them, the lorry driver followed him and I came last and closed the door. We were half way there.

The other half was to get them along the passage and up the tail board of the lorry. This had been sprinkled with straw, encouraging them to think it was the same surface as the pen they had left. The group of pigs trotted off towards the lorry and we followed enthusiastically. It looked like a good loading – until the driver ran alongside and hit the first one with the tattooing stick. A startled squeal burst from the shocked pig. The rest turned and bolted.

Dad stood with his hands on his hips.

'That was good. What other tricks do you do? Why didn't you wait until they were in the lorry?'

'Can't do them there,' the driver said, apologetically. 'Not enough room with the extra deck in. I can't stand up. They were going so quietly, I didn't think they'd bother.'

'Well, they did, didn't they?'

We looked at the group of pigs at the far end of the passage, clambering over each other.

'Yes,' the driver agreed.

We circled them quietly and brought them back along.

They were agitated. Once a pig loading goes wrong, it tends to stay that way.

'I've got to do them before they go in,' the driver repeated.

'Right,' Dad said, shortly. 'You'd better get them done then.'

The driver did what I would have done. He picked what looked like the quietest and, marginally, the smallest. He swung the stick heartily. I had never heard a pig yodel before. It rose vertically, trod air, hit the ground running and passed me like a whippet. It was an impressive performance.

We said nothing, but watched with interest. With nothing to lose now, he went for the biggest. It moved, and he missed. He swung, it moved, and he missed again. He approached carefully for a third time, and wound himself up like Lew Hoad about to serve at Wimbledon.

'What if . . .' I started to ask in a stifled whisper, but my question was answered before I had finished speaking. The driver walked forward as he swung. When the pig, a crafty rascal, moved at the last second, he couldn't stop his ferocious momentum. He tatooed himself perfectly, on his fleshy foreleg just above the left knee. For a second he looked at the heavy metal plate at the end of the thick, short handle, and couldn't speak.

'God, I've spiked myself,' he yelled, wakening to the pain, dropping the stick, and clutching his leg. He thought of rolling on the ground, but looked at the rich mix of pig muck, meal and straw and thought better of it.

'You're all right, man,' Dad said, picking up the tattooing stick. 'It's only a flesh wound.'

'It's not your leg,' the driver howled, hugging the affected limb.

'No,' said Dad, 'but they're my pigs, and we've been messing about here long enough.'

He strode up the passage, selected a pig, and smacked the tatooing stick against its shoulder. It grunted and moved aside. Briskly, he did the other five in the same way with no fuss. The driver stopped trying to clutch his leg to his stomach, and gingerly put his foot on the ground.

'How the hell did you do that?' he demanded, as Dad handed him back the stick.

'Because I know what I'm doing,' Dad replied, turning away.

The pigs, with a board behind them, trotted along the passage and straight up the ramp. We swung it into place behind them and fastened it. The driver hobbled out of the door with a few parting words of advice following him.

'Patience,' Dad said, 'remember that with pigs.'

The driver nodded dumbly, climbed into his cab, and drove away. Dad watched him go.

'How did you do it?' I asked.

'Luck. Pure luck. They could have gone anywhere, just the same as they did with him. Must have been my day. But he doesn't know that.'

He looked for a graip and brush to clear the doorway.

'If he shows the inspector that tattoo, I wonder if he'll qualify for a premium?'

The Dresser

It was all in the timing, I thought, lowering another sack over the ledge for the lorry driver to swing onto his shoulders. There was a skill in carrying 16-stone sacks of grain which had nothing to do with size.

There were two lorries in that morning for ten-ton loads of malting barley. The drivers helping each other could hardly have been more different. Little Tommy was five feet six inches, if he was lucky, and weighed under ten stones. Beefy, his mate, outweighed the sacks by several pounds.

Tommy eased the sack, which weighed more than half as much again as he did himself, into the precise centre of gravity of his back and shoulders, and trotted down the lorry. He seemed to shrug, rather than heave, his shoulders and the sack fell exactly where he meant it to go, completing a neat row across the lorry.

Beefy leaned back against the next sack I lowered to him. Sweat was trickling down his face. He grabbed the corners clumsily and pulled it forward. He stumbled awkwardly down the lorry, the sack slipping as he did so. It fell, rather than being guided, to start a new row. He spent some time dragging it across, and pulling it upright, barely finishing before Tommy arrived with the next, flipping it neatly into place.

I sympathised with Beefy. Tommy was an artist at that job. Not that I had much sympathy to spare, but I tried. It was my first year on the dresser.

The Hotel Lands steading we took over from Jean had a traditional granary, a two-storey stone building. The

bottom floor was in two sections, the top part in one, long and wooden-floored. We had nothing like it at the home farm. It meant extra road work during harvest, but gave us better handling facilities and extra storage space.

The granary upper floor was reached by the traditional flight of stone steps, on the outside, at one end. When men were men they carried 16 and 18 stone sacks up this flight of stairs from the threshing machine. We had no intention of doing that when the great design was schemed and built.

A pit was dug. A rectangular hole was made in the wall. The pit was lined with a triangular metal tank, with a shutter at the bottom. While it was being installed we had visitors, on a fishing holiday at the hotel.

The wife was brightly interested in this rustic engineering.

'Now,' she said. 'Tell me exactly what happens.'

Dad, anxious to get on, but polite, explained.

'The barley comes in here on a trailer from the combine. Reverse – tip the trailer – into this metal tank here.'

'There?'

'Yes.'

'And then what happens to it?'

'It goes through the shutter at the bottom and gets picked up by little scoops on a canvas belt – inside those pink wooden pillars.'

'It goes *up*?'

'Yes.'

'But why?'

'Because the dresser's upstairs.'

'I'm sorry – I'm rather confused.'

'I'm not,' said her husband.

'Well, *I* am. You want your – barley, was it? – you want that upstairs.'

'Yes.'

'So you tip it down into this metal thing?'

'Yes.'

'Why?'

'Dad was slightly on edge.

'Because the dresser's upstairs. That's where we sort the wheat from the chaff – or at least the barley from the awns.'

'But that doesn't explain why it goes down.'

'It has to go down, before it can go up. The only way to get it into the buckets is to tip it into the pit.'

'It's quite simple . . .' the husband started to say.

She looked at him. He said no more.

'I don't find it simple. I'm sure there's a perfectly good reason, but engineering is obviously beyond me. I only hope it works.'

'So do I,' Dad said to himself as they left. They turned back.

'Tell me,' she said. 'Why is all the wood painted that peculiar pink colour?'

'It's traditional,' Dad said. 'Threshing machines are painted that colour too.'

'I see. It's a most unusual pink I must say. Goodbye.'

The dresser itself was the same unusual pink. It was an enormous wooden construction which reached from floor to roof upstairs. I hated it.

I went in to the yard on harvest mornings already wearing a thin sheen of apprehension. My shirt sleeves were buttoned down, my collar up, and a handkerchief fastened tightly round my throat. I climbed the flight of stone steps more slowly than any man ever did carrying a 16-stone sack.

Dad skipped up them. He loved it in there. The clank of the buckets on the endless belt as they swung eternally round, dropping grain onto the series of sieves and riddles. The rustling, reciprocating rhythm of the sieves and riddles. The steady rush of grain, the throb of the whole machine which shook the fabric of the building and gave the floor a gentle, bouncing motion. And, over all, the thick haze of dust.

Not at first. Not when we went in. He would see the combine started first, checking that the morning dampness was off the crop and that the grain was hard and dry. He loved to be knee-deep in a ripe crop of good barley, rubbing heads of grain between his hands, blowing off the chaff and awns and inspecting the colour and texture of the grain left behind, biting it to test for moisture and quality.

Then the combine would start up. When we took over the 72 acre Hotel Lands farm, and the steading, we bought our own combine and took on an extra man.

'I was going to be a big farmer in my way of it,' Dad said later. It didn't quite work out that way, but the Hotel Lands takeover was an exciting time.

To my disappointment, the combine we bought wasn't self-propelled, as those we'd hired on contract for two years had been. It was pulled by a tractor, and driven by the power-take-off connection. It was a six-foot cut International with a grain collection tank.

This was a novelty because the contract combine had been a bagger. A man stood on a platform as the combine travelled, filling sacks with grain as it was cut. These were tied, and slid down a chute to the ground. From there, they had to be lifted onto trailers and carted into the shed. It always seemed a complicated way of doing things to me.

With our own combine there was no waiting for the contractor to arrive. With an extra man, Dad didn't need to drive the tractor and trailer. With our own grain-handling set up, even if it was at the other end of the village, we felt we were in business.

That was the combine he had started that morning. Jack was driving the blue Fordson Major which pulled it, massaging his shoulder as he drove because of the muscular strain put on it by having to wind the lift-handle up and down. Bill was on the trailer. His ambition was to drive down to the dresser with a load, and return empty, before Jack had a full tank and was sitting waiting. The trailer held about one and a quarter tons.

We were in the dresser, waiting for the first load. In it came. Dad pressed the electric buttons to start, first, the dresser then the buckets. Bill reversed, leapt out and opened the back door of the trailer, pulled the hydraulic handle up and shot the load into the depths of the pit. Immediately it began to flow through the half-open shutter and was collected by the buckets. Grain began to rattle onto the sieves. Dad grinned at the sound and hooked two sacks into place.

'Open the doors. Get a barrow. Cut another bundle of sacks open. It looks like nice barley.'

I opened the double-doors to let some air in. It was from here that we lowered sacks down onto lorries. A bundle of the thick, heavy, hessian sacks with British Rail stamped on them was cut open and laid out ready for use. I picked up the handles of the metal barrow ready for action.

The dresser was throbbing. Short straws, half heads,

ladybirds and caterpillars bounced out of one take-off spout into a bag. The lights of shrivelled grain, broken grain, and

tiny fragments of stone and grit came into another. These sacks were only changed periodically, their contents going to the deep litter hens.

The good-quality barley filled the 16-stone sacks, quickly. When one was full, Dad swung the shutter over to the replacement and swung the full bag, almost as easily, across the short space to the weights. It was important to get the weight, as it came off the dresser, as nearly right as possible. Precious time lost having to tip grain in, or even worse having to scoop it out, could lead to a backlog of problems.

He was meticulous about weighing.

'You can lose a lot getting it wrong. Old Geordie . . .'

He swung the bag off the weights ready for me to get

under with the barrow. He picked up an empty sack from
the bundle.

' . . . along the road, the steward, he had this old pan he
used for weighing. And when . . .'

He walked over and hooked the sack on. I started to
follow to hear what he was saying.

'. . . Take that one away. I'll tell you when you get back.'

I set off along the granary. I enjoyed this job. By mid-
harvest the wooden boards were as polished as a dance
floor by the continual traffic of feet and rubber wheels. All I
had to do was keep the sack balanced. If it fell too far back,
or too far forward, I was in trouble, sturdily built though I
was.

A 16 stone sack picks up momentum quickly. It wasn't
unusual to be jerked into the air as the sack fell forward,
then struggle to right it again. Through all this I would
keep tight hold of the neck. A spilt sack of grain was not
popular.

I set it in position, against the last of the previous day's
sacks, and trotted back. He was watching the last stone or
two of grain run in to the one on the dresser.

'Aye, old Geordie weighing. When it was just about
balanced . . .'

He stepped forward, unhooked another full sack and
kneed it across to the weights. The horizontal pendulum
swung almost level. He was delighted, shaking a few grains
in to balance it perfectly.

'Not bad, eh? The old man's not lost his touch yet. Now
old Geordie, when it was swinging like that, he'd plash in
whatever he had in the pan. That'll do her, he'd say."

I was ready to go with the barrow.

'Cost them a fortune. They weighed what the pan held
one day. About two pounds. Big place. Six hundred tons a
year in bags. Say six thousand bags . . .'

He liked this kind of mental arithmetic. He hooked the
bag on, listened to a slight rattle, decided it was nothing
important, and turned back.

'. . . so, six thousand bags, plashing in two pounds extra,

that's about five and a half tons a year and he's been doing it for thirty years . . . take that bag away . . .'

I walked briskly off. The dust round the dresser was beginning to thicken. As I passed the double doors I breathed the fresh air in, deeply, and fingered the handkerchief round my neck. I was starting to itch already.

'. . . doing it for thirty years, that's, say, 160 tons at today's prices, good malting barley, say £18 a ton, that's . . .'

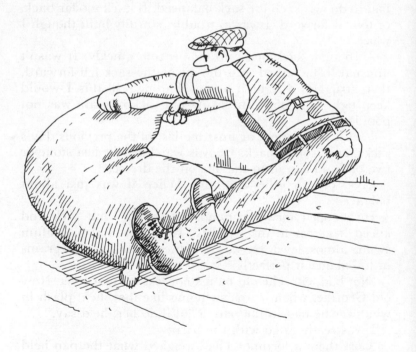

Another bag was full. The Ymer barley was dry and running through the dresser well and easily. That year we had Ymer, Beorna, Blenda and Procter. But he liked Ymer best.

'Grand sample. That'll interest Henry McCreath. So . . .

160 tons at £18 a ton . . . that's, let me see, £1800 – £900 – £180 – that's nearly £2,900. That's a lot of money.'

It would be about half our harvest income for that year. Poor old Geordie.

'Of course, on average he might only do it with half the sacks. Or maybe he bunged it in anyway. That is a nice sample.'

We settled into a routine. We always did, allowing for the occasional breakdown of a broken riddle, a stone jammed in the buckets, or a blocked sieve.

Sweat trickled down my back. Dust itched wherever I couldn't get at it to scratch. During the day I frequently soaked the handkerchief in cold water, often sticking my head under the brass tap in the yard, letting it flow and temporarily wash away the misery. My eyes were red and sore.

It wasn't sweated child labour. I stuck at it because I felt as if I was doing a man's job. It's an inbuilt conscience that the children of small businessmen grow up with. Work is life, life is work. The sooner you do something to help, the better.

Dust didn't trouble Dad at all. He was impervious to it. By later morning the sun was beating on the slates and he had stripped to a singlet, trousers and a coating of dust. It settled, and nestled, in layers, on the hair which covered his torso and shoulders. It caused him not the slightest concern. I itched just looking at him as he stood whistling in the worst of the stour, swinging off sacks, hooking on new ones and estimating yields.

In the same way he worked with bootfuls of barley. When I had barley in a boot I tiptoed about like a fakir doing a fire dance until I had a chance to take it off.

I was doing it now as I lowered the last of the sacks over the ledge, the thick hessian rubbing down the sun-warmed wall towards Beefy's trembling fingers and bent back. As soon as he seemed to have it, I pulled off my left boot and tipped out a few grains of barley. I stood up and wiped the sweat from my eyes as little Tommy methodically began to fasten ropes round his load.

I looked at the few golden-yellow grains on the polished floor. Dad would have ignored them. When we got into the house at night after a day on the dresser, clambering into the pit to release a jammed shutter, climbing into a trailer load to release the back door, or merely the amount which seemed to jump into boots from sieve, riddle and scales, he would tip what looked like half a pound of barley out of each boot.

His socks, stiff with barley awns, looked like dark green hedgehogs. His day's growth of beard bristled with dust. His deep-set blue eyes were rimmed with dirt and half-hidden.

He was perfectly happy.

Haircut

'You first.'

'Not me.'

'You go.'

'I'm not. It's your turn.'

'Come on,' Dad shouted through. 'I haven't got all night. One of you get through here.'

'Oh all right,' I muttered. 'I'll go.'

It was one more burden of responsibility of being the oldest. The choice was whether to go first and get it over with, or hang back and hope he would tire before it was my turn. I usually opted to go first to encourage the others. Whether it did nor not, as they listened to the squeak of the shears and the muffled squeals of the patient, is another matter.

I slunk out of the living room, where we had been huddled together arguing, into the kitchen where he was waiting. He flexed the hand-powered silver shears impatiently while I showed all the enthusiasm of a man going to be shot.

I walked across the kitchen floor to the wooden chair and straddled it, facing the back. It would have been easier to sit normally, facing the front, but that wasn't the accepted style. I put an old towel round my neck, and a weak smile on my face, and he made the first exploratory run with the shears into a rich, deep, undergrowth of hair.

He always said the same thing, probably without realising it.

'Only three days' difference between a good haircut and a bad haircut,' he said. 'Lift your head up. Don't duck down like that. You might lose an ear. Up – that's it.'

'Agh – ugh,' I gurgled.

'What?'

'Ah . . .ah . . .'

'Are they tugging a bit?' he asked, pulling the shears

123

away and raising them to eye level, inspecting the thick tufts of hair for signs of skin still attached.

'Ow . . . they are a bit,' I muttered.

The shears were hand-powered. The cutting action depended on his wrist power, squeezing the handles in and out. This power was considerable, but the general opinion at the hair-cutting post-mortem, as we walked to school the next morning, was that he couldn't sharpen them properly.

As we ruefully studied each other's tufted pates in the morning light, resembling small fields of barley after a gale, flattened and twisted in all directions with small plantations here and there, we knew he was wrong about the three days.

'Only three days' difference,' he said again, I suspect to reassure himself as much as me.

In my limited experience this difference could usually be counted as three weeks. In extreme cases, when he had sheared us in a hurry, or with a particularly blunt edge on the blades, it could be three months. Many of his theories had a sound basis, but this wasn't one of them.

'Oww . . .' I moaned again. I thought I heard a communal moan of sympathy from the corner, where the rest were beginning to gather.

'The door's locked,' he said. 'No one gets away.'

This was his little joke. The farmhouse doors, front and back, were never locked at any time. Even if we'd wanted to there were no keys to fit them. We might want to break out, but the thought of anyone breaking in didn't occur to us.

'What *is* it?' he asked testily, as I let out a full-blooded roar which had the gathering throng running for cover.

'You've cut my ear.'

'No such thing. Where?'

'There.'

I tried to indicate through what felt like a mouthful of loose hairs, and without using my arms which were trapped under the big old towel. I inclined my head towards my left shoulder, trying to show that it was my left ear.

He gave it a perfunctory glance.

'It's only a wee red mark. Nothing to worry about.'

'It's my ear,' I said resentfully.

'None of your cheek, lad. I'm not doing this because I want to. Sit quiet and I'll soon be finished.'

We had haircuts at home because it saved time and saved money. A mass Sunday night shearing session was part of growing up. It taught us the virtue of thrift, the value of doing a job yourself, and the meaning of pain.

I was sure it was what gave most of the family a high pain threshold. The pain of everyday cuts and bruises, nettle stings and thorn scratches, would be compared to the pain of a haircut. It gave the listener a clear idea of how severe it was.

'Remember the night the bit fell off the shears, and all the hair was coming out in big lumps, by the roots?'

'Yes?'

'Well, it was worse than that.'

'Ooh . . . that's bad.'

'I know. That's why I'm crying.'

The hurt was never meant, as hair wasn't so much cut as amputated and hauled out whimpering. But the uneven squeak of the shears, and low moans from the patient as tufts were uprooted, were met with the same polite indifference and occasional irritability.

Years of sheep shearing, removing wool from recalcitrant ewes, made hair cutting seem relatively straightforward. The bleats of both could be ignored and children were easier to restrain.

'That'll do. Sit still.'

I had been wriggling. This was met by a firm grip on the neck with one big hand, which tightened until the wriggling subsided, while the other kept the shears clicking away remorselessly, and clumps of hair fell to the ground.

We were getting to the tricky bit. There wasn't the luxury of a mirror, which was what I remembered from my only visit to a real barber. My grandad took me, when I was on holiday at the station, but it had been a disappointment.

The barber was a small, short-sighted man who used electric clippers. They seemed to be as badly set as the hand-shears I suffered at home. The only difference was that I could see what he was doing in the mirror, which seemed to increase the pain. He finished by slapping down the undergrowth that was left with a mass-produced version of Brylcreem out of a small barrel. He applied it in large dollops, and rubbed it in with gusto, humming to himself.

'There,' he said with satisfaction. 'You won't know Yourself.'

I felt like Toad of Toad Hall – a round, flushed face with a few short strands of hair slicked flat. I smelt like the perfume my grandmother used.

Dad was horrified.

'I doubt it'll take more than three days, right enough. That's barbarous.'

That was unintentional. Puns weren't in his line.

'You see now that you get a better haircut at home?'

Inspecting the damage in the small bathroom mirror, rising out of a clutter of toothbrushes, tubes, and soap, that seemed a moot point. But there wasn't much in it, I had to agree.

I remembered what the difference had been as Dad started to put the finishing touches to his handiwork. The barber had finished level on both sides of my head. Getting this balance always gave Dad a problem.

On a good night the right result might be achieved before the hair line rose too dramatically above my ears. Tonight there was no mirror, but I could tell from the draught that my hair-line was rising like the snowline on the Cheviot hills during a fast thaw.

My ears were being left far behind, like rock outcrops on a bare mountainside, with the occasional lonely patch of hairs like small plantations.

'That's it,' he said enthusiastically, with a final rapid stroke across the upper reaches of my skull, stepping back for a critical appraisal.

'No,' he growled, 'I'm damned if it is.'

He reached for the scissors and snipped rapidly round the edges. I squirmed hopelessly, in some danger of having an eye poked out or an ear removed.

'That's it,' he said again. And this time it was. I tottered away from the chair, ripping off the towel and beginning to appreciate again what a hair-shirt was. I spat hairs out and rubbed my eyes, which were already itching.

'Next,' Dad called, making a small adjustment to the shears with a screwdriver.

He looked critically at me.

'That's not bad,' he said. 'Not bad at all.'

As this was his highest form of praise for any human

effort, I was hopeful.

'Get under the tap,' he advised. 'The cold one.'

This did help. The main idea was that it would avoid a chill next morning when semi-bald head met chill winter.

I spluttered and splashed as I contorted my skull under the cold tap. Parts of me were going numb.

'It could be worse,' he said, starting on the next child. 'Sit still. Stop that.'

'How?' I asked, rubbing vigorously with a towel.

'There's a hill farmer I know – he sticks their head under a spout coming straight off the hill.'

'That'll kill them,' I gasped, as some feeling started to creep back into my numb skull.

'No, no, just what's needed. The sudden shock stops anything else affecting you.'

I could believe that. I ran a hand tentatively over the open spaces and wondered where some of the bumps had come from. The worst bit would be waking up in the morning and finding that what had been lying down was sticking up. I knew from experience it would look like a tussocky grass field, but there was nothing to be done about it now. That was it over for another few weeks, possibly months, if we were really busy on the farm.

I began to wander away as the shears started squeaking into action again.

'Don't jerk your head like that. Which one are you anyway, hiding under that towel. Oh. It's you. Well, stop jerking about. This won't take long. Three days and you'll never know the difference.'

Collies

Towards the middle distance a young dog was driving half a dozen small bullocks along the hedge. She had covered three fields to reach this stage, bringing two worried rabbits and a disgruntled pony with her, before reaching the bullocks.

The group of ewes she was meant to be collecting stood in a puzzled huddle in the far corner of the field. Dad sighed and rubbed the back of his head.

'One right way to train a collie – and a hundred and one wrong ways,' he said ruefully. 'I think I've tried most of them. Queen! You donnert little begger! Come by! Come by to me!'

Queen paid no attention. She was pleased with herself. The bullocks had settled to a steady gallop and she meant to keep them at it until she got tired or they died of exhaustion.

I thought of leaving. I had no ambition to train a dog, but twenty years of trying hadn't convinced Dad, and I never knew what to say when a collie was behaving badly. I wondered, when I saw some of his more explosive moments, if he was cut out for sheep and dog work at all.

He had been pitch-forked into it in his mid-teens, when his father told him: 'Tom, you'll be looking after the sheep

from the May term. I'm having to pay off the shepherd.'
To which he replied: 'Well, I'll need a horse to do it.'
That was that. Sheep and dogs, two of the most frustrating animals extant, were what he came to know best. In his first winter as a shepherd he was herding more than 400 ewes, and feeding several hundred hoggs on turnips.

He shot his first dog for worrying sheep. Ewes died, as they do, during lambing. Lambs died from what was called 'wool ball' in the stomach. The real reason was pulpy kidney, a disease now readily controlled with vaccine.

What puzzled me was why, with this start, he decided to keep sheep when he farmed on his own and had a choice. I don't think it ever occurred to him not to. Lambing, shearing, selling, tupping, feeding were part of the fabric of his life. For all their frustrations, he couldn't see life without them, an enthusiasm I never shared.

With the sheep came the dogs, much the same size and shape through the years, but with very different temperaments.

Queen, the one we watched as she set the bullocks off on a third circuit of the field, was volatile.

She always ran five times further than she needed to. After that, with luck on a good day, she herded in what she was supposed to. On a bad day she tackled the wrong stock, as she was doing now, partly because she preferred cattle to sheep and partly because she was half-cracked.

Apart from hyper-activity, she detested any dog bigger than herself. This gave her an active life, because most other dogs were bigger and resented Queen going for their throat without so much as a warning bark.

Her main victim was Tommy Carr's Airedale, itself a noisy, aggressive brute which the haulier kept for guard duty. No one was sorry about Queen's attacks on him, except the Airedale, which was big, rough and stupid.

As Queen got older she became a clever strategist, substituting intelligent counter-attack for the frontal assaults of her puppyhood. She looked forward to a visit to Carr's Yard where, among the lorry wheels, parked cars, undergrowth, old oil drums, tyres and shreds of canvas sheet, she would take the Airedale to the brink of a nervous breakdown.

She would do this by hiding, racing out to sink her teeth into the Airedale's woolly hide, then racing back under cover. From underneath a parked car, she would grin ferociously at his snarling, frothing face as he tried to jam his bulk underneath. He was an animal with a short attention span and would soon turn away in disgust. When he did, Queen shot out and bit him again. She could keep it up for as long as Dad was in the yard and the Airedale got no wiser as it got older.

Tommy Carr would watch the antics of both dogs with a preoccupied expression, while talking.

'Your collie's going to get hurt one of these days, Tom,' he used to say. But she never did. When the Airedale died, a little bit of zest went out of Queen's life. Nothing else was quite so satisfying to bite.

Dad managed to intercept Queen towards the end of the third lap with a well-aimed stick, which threw her off her stride. He dropped to his knees as she grovelled towards us, tail dragging and wagging pathetically at the same time.

Dropping to his knees wasn't a prayer of thankfulness. It was to get a better grip on her throat, where one hand twitched while the other formed a massive fist under her nose. It was a pause too deep for words. Nothing was said as they looked deep into each other's eyes. He let go and stood up.

Queen, in relief, rolled apologetically on her back and grinned with her long pink tongue hanging out.

'Put it away or I'll cut if off,' he said, giving her an exasperatedly affectionate slap. 'I'll have to get the old one.'

'Fan?'

'How many old ones have we got? At least she goes in the right direction.'

'But you never know for how long.'

Fan had developed an original stop and start technique, as premature old age caught up with her. The call of nature in a prolonged form never affected her until she was half-way through a gather.

On the brink of success, when it seemed easier to go on than to stop, she would stop. She would squat thoughtfully for minutes, ignoring sheep and pleading shepherd alike. This squat helped her considerably and was diverting for the casual spectator, but did absolutely nothing for the shepherd's temper.

Dad shouted and whistled, sheep scattered and ran, Fan squatted until she felt comfortable again. It was when he broke a second crook over his knee that he decided to train another dog.

Patience is needed to train a collie. Brute force and bad language help the trainer a little, but do nothing for the dog. What it needs is patience and tender, loving care and attention. Not a lot of dogs get that, but it's what they need.

He had too many small chores and major worries to make a good dog trainer or handler. Too many other things were waiting to be done to get the best out of a dog which ran in the wrong direction, or covered three extra fields from sheer exuberance.

He wasn't alone in his efforts to get a dog to do what it was told. On a clear morning I have heard three shepherds roaring in unison from their respective hills, like bull moose in the mating season.

'Are there any good sheep dogs?'

'Good dogs? Of course there are. There aren't any bad dogs – only bad handlers.'

'Well, why . . .'

'Some are a bit better than others, of course.'

I thought hard.

'I don't remember us having any good ones.'

This was a body blow to him.

'Of course we have. Fan was good until she started this business of stopping half way round.'

'But she bites them as well.'

'Not much. Not bites. Nips a bit when they need it to get them moving.'

'But that one the other day was bleeding . . .'

'All right. She just misjudged it. Stop nattering on.'

We walked steadily back towards the steading, Queen trotting behind, keeping close to heel and taking no chances.

'I knew a man that bought a book on dog training once,' he said suddenly. 'The dog he was trying to train ate it. Another chap I knew lost his temper with a dog.'

He mentioned this as if it was a rare occurrence. I waited for the rest of the story.

'Lost his temper completely and dragged it off to the dipper on the other side of the field. He came back a few minutes later without the dog.'

There was more to come.

'He said he thought the temper would be off him by the time he got the dog there – but it wasn't.'

I gaped.

'You mean – he drowned it?'

'That's what he did. I've shot one because I had to, but I wouldn't drown one.'

He turned to look at Queen, who shuffled onto her bottom again.

'At least I don't think I would.'

Queen wasn't the first, the worst or the last we would have.

'What about that one that peeed on your leg. And mine?'

When I thought about it I could still feel the hot stream trickling down my leg into my sock and boot, and see the dog giving its leg a contented shake and trotting away.

'Just a trick it had. It soon got over it.'

As far as we knew. He'd sold it.

'And that one that liked rolling in muck.'
'I know. It was the friendliest dog we ever had.'

He let Fan out of the kennel and she spun round several times in the sunlight, bumping and rushing about with Queen. The activity reminded me of the only time I had been to a sheepdog trial.

The sight of dogs responding to a series of whistles, moving left or right, stopping and starting according to signal, was a novelty.

Driving home we found it difficult to think of one of ours which, in full flight, could be persuaded to stop by anything more subtle than a blow on the head.

Considering what I knew at home, and shepherds I had seen, I didn't put a lot of faith in the saying that a dog is man's best friend. But I admired their perseverance.

We got back to the field. I held Queen back with a piece

of string as she valiantly tried to choke herself and join Fan.

Fan, on the outrun, was working well. The day was improving. She began the gather. The sheep were moving steadily together, moving towards us, heading for the gate we wanted them through. I turned, with Queen, to walk across and open it. Half way there I heard the explosion. I didn't need to look. I knew what Fan would be doing.

She was. She squatted comfortably with an intent expression on her grey-muzzled face. Dad was addressing her from a distance. The ewes with nothing to urge them on were starting to look round and disperse.

I kept walking towards the gate. It semed the right thing to do at the time.

Growing

With a pedigree of large, inter-married farming families behind us, we had dozens of relatives. A visit for us usually only meant a change of farm, but we had to pick our targets carefully. Only certain relatives could stand more than one visit a year.

The relatives came into many categories – close, distant, pleasant, barely speaking, young, elderly and two small groups, those poorer than us and the very rich. This last class had a membership of one couple, rich, elderly and childless.

We made ritual visits there, carrying gifts of butter and honey because Uncle seemed to expect them. We knew he was rich because he wore plus fours and a straw hat, and smoked cigars.

There was no nonsense about equality in that elegant farmhouse. Our parents were allowed to take tea in the drawing room. We weren't. Children weren't heard and, whenever possible, weren't seen either. We packed round the scullery table eating bread and butter under the keen eye of a maiden sister.

It was good for the soul, no doubt, but not calculated to

make us like him. Aunt, gentle and kindly, missed the censure, but forty years of smoothing life's path for Uncle, meant never going against his wishes.

If undetected after tea we gathered at the celestial globe, which stood at the foot of the stairs. We played with it until tired, or someone jammed their fingers, whichever came soonest. It was usually the fingers. The roar of pain saw us dispatched outside. Often we were dispatched before we got as far as the globe, as an affront to an orderly house.

In summer, if in season, we were allowed into the net-covered strawberry patch. Three strawberries each, and out. Many a blessing was heaped on the head of that good old man.

Luckily, there were other relatives. At Cauldshiel, it always seemed to be full house, by the day or by the week, and we simply joined the flow, playing riotous games of snap on the big table or equally riotous games of rough croquet on the big lawn.

Angus and I spent our first holidays away from home there, loving it by day, but slightly home-sick at nights, lying in strange beds, listening to the pines rustling in the wind, with a tiny lingering ache until the day the big, green Morris traveller drove up the farm road.

It had been brought to transport nine of us, on major expeditions, in comfort. It was the size of a small bus and needed to be, because soon there were ten. The year I left home, Donald was born.

There was no connection between the events. It only felt as if I was leaving home and that the first holidays on my own had been a practice run. I left home by the week, from Monday morning until Friday night, when I started at the grammar school some miles away.

From a maelstrom of children, surrounded by farm and familiarity, I went to a semi-detached in town owned by an elderly lady with strong views on bed times and behaviour. Her other lodgers were an overweight, genteelly alcoholic banker and a young professional lady who kept to herself.

It improved as the months went by, but on the first

Friday I was at the bus station half an hour before the only bus of the late afternoon left. I climbed aboard as soon as it drew up and waited, fretfully, for it to leave town. Because the conductor refused to see the wood at the farm roadend, it was several hundred yards further on before I got the driver to stop.

I jumped off violently, and ran back, the satchel bumping on my back, socks rolled down, tie hanging loose. They were there. Four of them, in the dusk, waiting for me.

'Here he is.'

'It's him. I told you he'd be here.'

'What's it like not being at home?'

'What's wrong with your eyes?'

'Bit of dust off the bus. It's okay. School's okay. Is Dad combining?'

He was. I changed as quickly as I could then, ungraciously leaving the others behind, I ran down the Big Hill in darkness and gathering dampness. They were cutting a final strip of spring barley before finishing for the night and I could see him, in the tractor lights, characteristically biting and inspecting grains.

He looked up, as I arrived, panting.

'Hello, boss. Have a good week?'

'Yes.'

'Grand. Climb into the trailer, and you'll get a lift up.'

Donald was born some months later, an arrival which coincided with our first television set. A vote on whether the new baby, or the screen which brought us Sergeant Bilko, I Married Joan, Burns and Allan, David Nixon and nightly news, was most popular would have been a close one.

I always associated his arrival more closely with ginger beer. It was home made the previous summer, to a patent recipe which involved boiling, mixing and adding various ingredients, then corking the bottles tightly. That was an important instruction. We boiled, mixed, added and corked, then set them to rest in the old, damp, peeling pantry at the end of the passage.

Dad was reaching for a scone when we heard the first

explosion. He paused, and cocked his head. The chattering and arguing at the bottom end of the table faded away. The second explosion was followed by the sound of falling glass.

'What's that?'

'Somebody's shooting at us!'

'Don't be silly.'

He had pinpointed the sound by then and, once round the corner of the passage, was guided by the reek of ginger beer. He came back holding the neck of a bottle.

'Powerful stuff. I don't think any more will go off.'

A third explosion rocked the pantry. He pushed his plate away.

'All right. We'll move them now.'

He advanced cautiously along the passage, and opened the door. The erupting cork had shattered a jam jar on the opposite shelf.

'Too tightly corked,' he said. 'The corks should've been left slightly out for a few days until it stopped fizzing.'

'But it said . . .'

'But we were told to . . .'

'But Mum said to . . .'

'All right. All right. Let's get them outside. Out of the way.'

He carried them out, wrapped in a towel, like hand grenades. Once in the yard, we studied the murky orange contents with froth forming below the corks.

'I bet it could hit the byre door.'

'From here?'

'Aye.'

'I bet it wouldn't.'

'Watch.'

I gave the bottle a shake it didn't need, having eased the cork out slightly. I held it grimly, in the towel, and pointed it along the yard, aiming at the circle painted on the door which we used for our own version of basketball. Abruptly, the fizzing and frothing in the bottle sent the cork along the yard like a bullet. A blast of ginger beer splattered the door fifteen yards away.

'Gosh!'

'Told you.'

'Let me try.'

The door still smelt of ginger beer when it was taken off its hinges a few months later, as the old byre and bothy were pulled down.

It was the explosions which had worried Dad slightly.

'Good job it didn't give your mother too big a fright.'

'Why?'

'She's having another baby.'

'When?'

'A few months.'

'Oh.'

Children weren't allowed in to the maternity home, but a kind nurse arranged for us to stand outside while she opened the curtains, briefly, from the inside. We stood in a row, bigger ones holding up the smaller, looking in to where Dad stood beside the bed and Mum was holding a small, red faced baby.

Fiona, Katrine, Angus, Ailsa, Elspeth, Sheelagh, and myself exchanged glances. Did all babies look like that?

Dad assured us, on the drive home in March darkness, that they did. We had all looked like that in our early days.

'Did you like him?'

'Yes.'

I still connected the new arrival with the smell of ginger beer, but forgot that as Dad said, casually:

'I thought we might get a television set for your mother coming home.'

'Smashing!'

'Will we get Andy Pandy?'

'Yes.'

'And the cup final?'

'Yes.'

'Can we afford it?'

'Yes. Now sit quiet – we'll soon be home.'

Home – the word had a solid ring to it. With a new baby and a television on the way it seemed that it might be permanent.

Lambs

I only knew two Captains. There was the old landlord I only saw once. The other was our next farm neighbour.

He was the one who cantered past on his morning outing, as we drove ewes and lambs up the farm road towards the sheep pens at the steading. He seemed to fit the bill of one of the stories I had read recently, 'a decent old buffer,' with his thin, reddish face, riding breeches and boots, hacking jacket, and cap square on his head. He reined in to talk to Dad.

'Morning. Clipping?'

'Morning, Captain. No, cutting lambs.'

'Ah. Gelding 'em, eh? When do you start clipping?'

'A few weeks yet.'

'Do 'em yourself?'

'Yes.'

'So does Walter. Hundreds of 'em.'

He leant over to study me more closely, in my old school shirt, worn trousers, and heavy boots.

'That would knock the roses out of your cheeks, eh, lad?'

I flushed and nodded. He was only doing his best to be pleasant. He raised his hand. We kept walking up the road behind the flock, little pellets of dung spattering among the ballast and dust as they bleated their way along, with the May morning mist already clearing and the sun striking through.

The sheep smell hung heavy in the air, an unmistakable acrid sharpness. There was only one road the sheep could follow, so it was a pleasant walk behind them.

Dad watched the Captain trot out of view.

'He's smiled like that ever since his horse finished the Grand National.'

'Won it?'

'No, just finished the course. I think it was sixth. They say he was into the pictures three nights in a row, watching the Pathe news film of the race.'

'What's he like?'

'The Captain? Nice enough chap. Always been fair with me. But God knows what he did to get a double hernia.'

'A what?'

'Double hernia. You usually get it with lifting something heavy. I had one once. That was trying to carry 18-stone wheat bags up those granary steps at Ellingham.'

'I remember that. I remember them carrying you out the door of the cottage into the ambulance. I'd be about four.'

'Funny you should remember. I think they'd probably be carrying me back in after the operation. Anyway, I got it carrying heavy weights. How he got two is a mystery.'

He thought for a minute. We were getting near the brow of the hill, and the leaders among the ewes picked up speed as the road seemed to open before them.

'You wouldn't think riding a horse would be the best thing for a man with a truss. He could ride a camel.'

Several of the children were waiting at the top of the road. The dogs swept the flock round the corner into the yard, and then into the pens, which ran between the tractor shed and the old stone wall.

Dad set out his equipment, starting with the cut-throat razor. He gave it a final rub on the stone. There was a shiny metal tube and spring, to pop a worming pellet down each lamb's throat, and a syringe and penicillin for any which had a boil, lump, tail maggots or any of the other handicaps from which lambs suffered occasionally. There was also a marker of thick, greasy, blue crayon in a metal container to identify them, if necessary, a bucket of hot water, with Dettol in it, to wash the razor at intervals, and a pair of pliers.

It was set out neatly at his side of the narrow catching pen. Between us, we dropped the first lamb. It knocked over the bucket, trampled the equipment and shot into the yard blaring its head off, with Queen close behind. We looked at each other accusingly.

'I thought you had it.'

'I didn't want it. I'm expecting you to hold them.'

'Sorry.'

'Never mind. We'll get it in a minute.'

We got it sooner than that, because Queen hounded it back beside us in seconds. It cannoned round the pen, like a hard-hit billiard ball, before I caught it and hurled it back into the catching pen, in-off the rails.

'Don't be too rough on them. Gently does it.'

I climbed back into the catching pen. Lambs were about my going. I could catch and handle them, or at least most of them. Some of the biggest ones, the February mistakes which were the result of an eager ram reaching the ewes too early, were difficult. I struggled and puffed getting them into a sitting position on the rail.

Once there, my head was in position beside theirs, while I adjusted my grip, catching their back legs with my hands and pulling them upwards. This left their tails and, in the case of ram lambs, their testicles exposed to Dad and the razor.

I could feel the woolly bodies trembling against me, exertion not panic. They couldn't know what they had to panic about. The brown eyes were usually round and wide open. Few of them made a sound as Dad made his swift, clinical slices with the razor.

I half-squinted at the operation, in sympathy.

'Doesn't it hurt?' I asked.

'Only if you cut your finger,' he replied, slitting through the soft skin of a lamb's cod and expertly pulling out the two small, pink testicles. He flicked them into a bucket, for the dogs. He held the tail with one hand and cut sharply through it with the razor in the other. I dropped the lamb to the ground, on the theory that this sudden shock made them forget the pain. It bounced, all four legs stiff, and bleated for the first time. Still bleating, it stotted away to find its mother.

Dad dropped the tail onto the heap for ram lambs. That way, we got an exact count of males and females. That had been the last one in the catching pen, and we paused for a breather.

He lit a cigarette.

'I used to pull them out with my teeth – when I had them all. When I got the false ones at the front, it wasn't so handy.'

I goggled.

'Pull what out?'

'The stones, Cut the end off the cod, bend down and catch them with my teeth and pull. I got a far better grip than I do with this.'

He waved the saw-toothed, plier-like device in his hand almost derisively. It seemed to work well enough to me.

'Funny thing,' he said thoughtfully, as we worm-dosed our way through the next batch before starting to cut them, 'cutting their tails and stones off quite often stops them scouring.'

He looked more thoughtful.

'It would probably have the same effect on me.'

We cut away steadily for most of the morning. The standard joke was that the operation must be harder on ram lambs, because they bounced away two stones lighter. Except for the occasional rig, with only one stone, or for the even more occasional lamb which refused, very wisely in my view, to lower its testicles at all.

'How the hell do they do that,' Dad said, in aggravation, after we had spent several minutes trying to coax a small, hairy lamb to lower the necessary appendages. It consistently refused. We had to let it go, reluctantly, marked conspicuously with thick blue crayon.

'He must be holding his breath,' said Dad. 'It's the only explanation. They're hiding in there somewhere. That's just the sort of little runt that'll give us trouble. If he's still here in October he'll be trying to tup anything that lies down.'

Eventually, we were through them. Dad straightened up, wiped the razor and a spasm crossed his face.

'The pets,' he said.

I was half over the fence, looking forward to dinner time.

'What?'

'The pet lambs. We forgot them.'

'Are we doing them?'

It hardly seemed fair. There were five small, pot-bellied, survivors of the annual crop of orphan lambs, running about in the croft with the house cow.

They were orphans for a variety of reasons, most of them annoying. Their mother might have died, or might not have had enough milk, or might have knocked them off for no good reason other than awkwardness. They might even have known more than one mother. One, particularly unfortunate, had suffered this way.

Buffeted severely by three mothers in succession, he had become a pet. He was the one who bleated loudest, drank fastest and sucked hardest at his black-teated bottle.

It was the sucking of large quantities that made pet lambs pot bellied. On mother's milk, they headed for the bar many times a day, little and often. Pet lambs, in the early days of lambing, also got fed little and often, but the intervals lengthened and quantities increased with the workload.

Our enthusiasm waned at the same time. When the first pet lamb came out of the Aga in a box, there would be a fight to see who got to feed it. The novelty value meant that this fierce competition would continue for approximately twelve hours. After that, feeding pet lambs was one more chore.

They slavered and slobbered at their bottle. Weakly ones would have difficutly in sucking at all, but bully boys yanked the teat from the bottle, and soaked themselves and the feeder in warm, sticky milk. Trying to feed two at once was tricky, although three could be managed by also holding a bottle between the knees. This was known as showing off and usually ended with half a pint of milk inside a wellington instead of a lamb.

Pet lambs never thrived as well as they should have done. Artificial milk wasn't as good as mother's. Their wool was stiff and dull. They scoured and piddled extravagantly.

Even on fresh straw, they smelt.

But the worst thing was that they never accepted bottle-feeding days were over. Going into the croft to bring in Billy, the cow, meant being ambushed by five frenzied pet lambs, convinced that there was a bottle of milk secreted on my person.

It was no problem to get them into the pen, only a matter of opening the gates and calling 'Suck, suck – suck, suck.' This was the call we used for all sheep, and there was a tendency to run the 'sucks' together, so much so that a visitor once asked: 'Why do you call your sheep "sexy, sexy"?'

The five potbellied lambs ran in to the pen. I picked up

the first one and swung it over the rail.

'This is going to hurt me more than it hurts you,' I said, not believing it.

It didn't take long. The startled 'Baw!' in my right ear was the loudest of the day, so loud I almost dropped him, but the flickering razor was too fast even for him. We shooed the five back to the croft, squirting small fountains of blood, before we had time to feel sorry for them.

I found an old potato sack and counted the tails into it, squirming a little at the warm, squashy softness, often able to remember which lamb they came from. There were 107 ram lambs and 118 ewe lambs, including the pets.

'Not bad,' Dad said, 'that's about 195 per cent lambing in that field. Mind you, it started off as all twins. We've still got the singles to cut. Not bad, though.'

It's a mistake to think that sheep think like we do. It's a mistake to think that sheep think. All five pets were nibbling grass, and as I stopped to look at them over the gate, they came up and started bleating and nuzzling for milk. Their tails were already drying up.

'It's quick and clean,' Dad said, 'they don't even realise they've gone.'

'Everything go all right?' Mum asked, pouring the potatoes.

'Yes,' I said, 'we didn't cut ourselves at all.'

'Yes,' Dad said, waiting to get into the sink to wash his hands, 'we seemed to get the knack of it right away.'

Elevator

'It's the latest thing,' Dad said.

'How does it work?'

He looked at me with slight exasperation.

'It's an elevator.'

'I can see that.'

'Which fits on to the tractor. At the side.'

'How?'

He pointed to some metal bars and bolts.

'We bolt those on to the tractor. Right? This bit sticks up straight – I think – and the elevator fastens on to it.'

I inspected the bits, trying to look as if I knew what I was looking for.

'That's surely clear enough?' he said.

'I don't see why we want it on the side of the tractor.'

He looked at me closely, bafflement taking over from exasperation.

'You're not stupid.'

It was a statement, not a question.

'No, but . . .'

'You do all right at school. Not as well as you should, but all right.'

'Yes, but . . .'

'So why can't you see something as plain as your nose?'

'I'm trying to,' I shouted. Trivial differences seemed to lead to shouting more often these days. I was almost fifteen.

'Look. Start again. The elevator is to pick up bales.'

'You didn't say that. I thought it was to put them in to the hayshed.'

'It is.'

'But you just said . . .'

He was shouting now.

'It is to put them in the hayshed. And it's to pick them up in the field. That's what I'm trying to tell you!'

'Ah.'

'You'll see when we try it. I hope.'

We stamped off in different directions.

We tried it for the first time in the Little Baldrons hay. It looked an impressive set up.

Angus was rowing the hay up for the last time, with the little Fergie and the six-wheeled turner, each wheel consisting of flexible finger-like tines.

Jack was baling with the red International tractor and baler. The row of hay was pulled in by rotating wire fingers, thumped into shape in the chamber by the powerful ram, and pushed through. String passed round each bale as it went. Knotters tied the strings, and cut them at the knot, ready for the next. The completed bale reached the end of the chamber and popped out onto the ground. One fell every dozen yards or so as it was a good crop. This was where we came in, with our impressive-looking set up, a few rows behind.

I drove the blue Fordson Major, with the elevator attached alongside. Dad had had some trouble with the two-stroke engine, but it was now coughing and spluttering happily, blowing fumes into the open cab. Metal guides at each side extended the mouth of the elevator to make bale gathering easier. A tin shelf at the top guided the bale to the man building them onto the trailer.

I drove carefully into the first row and approached the first bale. Dad waited, expectantly, on the trailer.

The bale skidded along the ground as the elevator chattered away at it, pulling out small chunks of freshly-baled hay with the sets of ribbed teeth on every fifth wooden slat. Finally, it turned sideways and jammed completely, as we reached the next bale in the row. I stopped and jumped out. Dad got off the trailer.

'You'll have to line it up straighter.'

'I did line it up straight. It wouldn't go on.'

'You've got to be dead in line.'

'I can't. They don't fall out of the baler like that.'

'Right. Fine. You can't do it.'

'I could if they lay straight.'

That seemed an idea. He waved violently to Angus, who had just finished rowing up and parked the tractor and turner.

'Angus. Come over here and line the bales up straight for the elevator.'

'It'd be easier throwing them onto the trailer, the same way we did before,' I said, showing a penchant for progress.

'No, it wouldn't,' he said shortly. We discussed it no further.

He got back on to the trailer. I got back on to the tractor. Angus set off to pull bales into position. This time it

worked. The elevator picked them off the ground and they
flew upwards, at great speed. Dad pulled them off at the
top, starting to build them into place. He looked like a man
who'd won a raffle, and stuck his thumb in the air when I
looked round.

We travelled steadily down that row and up the next.
The load grew, layer by careful layer. There was no
conversation. The tractor was only ticking over, in low
gear, but the two-stroke elevator engine drowned out
everything else.

Angus had cut across into the next row, as the elevator
picked up the last bale of the row we were in and I started
to turn. This was a mistake.

As I inched steadily round, taking care not to turn too
sharply, I thought I heard a noise above the elevator
engine. But it came and went, and I couldn't be sure.
Somehow, I got the feeling all was not well. When Angus
appeared beside the tractor, like a jumping jack, waving his
arms and leaping up and down, I knew that feeling was
correct. Faintly, I could hear a bellow above the engines. I
stopped, and looked round.

The carefully built load was at a steep angle towards the
far side of the trailer. By craning my neck, out and
upwards, I could just see Dad. He was perched perilously
on the tin slide at the top of the elevator, narrowly avoiding
the slapping wooden slats as they whirred round. He'd only
managed to stay there by hurling the last two bales onto the
ground. I couldn't hear what he was shouting, but I knew
by his expression it wasn't best wishes.

'What do I do,' I roared.

Angus waved towards the right. I moved that way, and
gradually the load returned towards the level. I stopped the
tractor, jumped out, choked the elevator two-stroke, and
waited. He climbed, a little stiffly, down the silent elevator.

'Why didn't you stop?'

'I couldn't hear for the elevator.'

'I was bawling my head off. I was nearly off. You might
have looked round.'

'I was watching the bales.'

'You have to look round on a job like this.'

'What happened anyway?'

'It was when we raised the elevator as high as it would go at the far end. See, the way the delivery slide points to the left.'

'Ah. I see – when the load got as high as the slide . . .'

'Aye – when it got as high as the slide, you shouldn't have turned to the right. It started pushing into the load.'

'You weren't half shouting,' Angus said.

'I know. I couldn't believe it when you kept turning.'

'I couldn't hear you.'

'I might have been killed.'

'Sorry,' I grunted.

Enough had been said on the subject. He kicked an elevator tyre which looked a bit soft.

'Not quite what I thought it would be,' he said.

When he started to criticise his own ideas, I felt obliged to stick up for them.

'It wasn't that bad – once we got the hang of it.'

'Well, we'll see. Let's take this load up.'

We unhitched the elevator. Jack was still baling across the field.

'We'll have to carry them into heaps if we don't get them led tonight.'

We drove out of the Baldrons, across the Bog, and through the gate, which was standing open. It concertinaed, before my disbelieving reactions could stop the tractor. The catch for the elevator, jutting out a foot beyond the tractor wheel, had scythed into it. I shut my eyes, and waited for the blast from behind.

'Never mind,' he sighed, from where he stood on the drawbar, 'reverse, and I'll pull it out the way. It's been that sort of day.'

Clipping

I liked clipping time. I threw another greasy, rolled up, fleece into the big woolsack, hung on ropes between two rafters, and turned to watch Dad.

He was competent, rather than prize winning, for style or speed, but made up for it with effort. I didn't know that then. He looked good to me, as sheep came out of the catching pen, thickly-fleeced, and trotted out the door several minutes later minus their wool, but plus the occasional cut and nick.

'I've done worse things shaving,' he would say, if a particularly large section of skin was removed by the electric clippers, giving it a squirt of oil to keep the flies off.

I'd rolled fleeces for a year or two, but now I was catching as well, another rung on the job ladder. The previous year our big Half-bred ewes, a regular cross between the Border Leicester and the Cheviot, had still been too big for me. This year I could match them – with a struggle. The biggest seemed like camels as I tried to guide them to the small exit gate where Dad waited, impatiently when fresh in the morning, more tolerantly later in the day when he needed a breather.

The trick, if there was one, was to let the sheep do the work. Grabbing one by the head was useless. They simply dug their toes in and refused to move. Pushing was no better. They twisted round and escaped. The best way was to get one hand under their jaw, as a guide, and the other hand as near the tail as possible. For a young teenager with short arms and a Half-bred ewe with a telescopic neck, it wasn't easy.

I persevered. Sweat ran down my face, I wished I'd had a haircut and thought of asking for a trim, my boots slipped among the sawdust and grassy sheep droppings, but I kept at it. No one likes to quit on a new job.

Once at the gate, which I manoeuvred open while

152

pressing the ewe against the side, they were keen to get out. Dad caught them as they went past, under the chin, in the same way as I had just let them go.

He usually caught and couped them cleanly. A rare, headstrong type might try to make it to the door, with him hanging on grimly and muttering about his shoulder, but only one ever got there.

It was the biggest ram we ever had, an Oxford Down. They are a big breed, and this was a big specimen of it.

It was the size of a small donkey. Turning it onto its tail to clip it at all was a feat. Holding it there, when it started to kick, was impossible. That came when he was trying to lower it to full length, on its side. It got disgruntled and stood up. Once it found it could get up, it started to move.

Dad said later that he was taken aback. One look at his face, as the ram rose from the clipping sheet like a whale from the deep, told me that. It was too far away to intercept or, looked at another way, far enough not to get trampled.

He had been kneeling astride the tup, one leg against the backbone, the other knee pressed firmly into the flank, as he prepared to give the finishing touches. Instead, the ram stood up and walked out. He lay along its back with an expression, which started as amusement, but didn't last. One leg jogged the ground as the tup saw daylight and gathered speed, trailing several yards of attached fleece and a volley of bad language.

It hit the doorway at full gallop, Dad at that stage still trying to pull himself back into position, like an unseated jockey, to restrain it. He was handicapped by not having reins, and even more by facing the wrong way. I didn't see him fall off, but I heard. I guessed he wasn't pleased. I pulled the cord, to stop the chattering clippers he had abandoned, and ran outside.

He was dusting down his trousers, feeling a rib, and watching the Oxford mill about among the clipped ewes in the top corner of the yard.

'Big sod,' he said.

With the aid of a gate, we jammed the ram in a corner.

Dad sliced off what was left of the fleece with the hand shears, and stuck them under the ram's nose.

'Cut your throat if you do that again,' he remarked. I picked up the remnants of the fleece, and we fastened together what we could.

Nothing as entertaining had happened for a year or two. Today all had gone well. I worked up a lather bringing them out of the pen, he worked up a lather clipping them.

First he sat them on their bottom on the thick stack sheet, nestling against his legs. He wore old flannels, boots, and a singlet.

Getting them to sit comfortably was to be half way there. If they were uncomfortable, they kicked and fidgeted.

Clipping

'Sit still, you scraffling old bitch,' he murmured.

With the sheep sitting peacefully, the first move was down the side of the cheek, in to the neck wool to open it up. Then the belly and the potentially hazardous area round the udder, before clearing one side with increasingly long strokes, putting his back into it and stretching his thighs. With one side sheared, and lying free, his feet and legs adjusting their grip all the time, the move was made to lower the sheep to clip the other side.

This was when it was easiest to lose control, as the Oxford found. Once down, and still under control, the final sweeps were made along the back. With the final stroke, the sheep stood up and walked away, leaving the fleece. Some walked away, as if not quite clear what had happened to them, some bolted, some were like lambs and bounced out stiff-legged.

While he was clipping, I rolled the previous fleece. To do this I threw it out like a tablecloth cut side down, on another piece of clean sheet. Picking the longest piece of wool, usually from that first cut down the neck, I stretched this out at one end. The sides of the fleece were turned in. The whole fleece was then rolled up like a piece of carpet, as tightly as possible, and the neck wool twisted, equally tightly, into a rope. This was wound round the rolled fleece, and tucked in under itself.

In theory, I now had a tidy rolled fleece. In practice, the big Half-bred fleeces would threaten to fall apart at their open fibres, or the rope would disintegrate. I packed them into the woolsack as quickly as possible.

Lanolin in the wool gave my hands a thick, greasy, sheen. A hidden thorn in one fleece had left an irritating scratch. My trousers, and face, shone with greasiness.

By the time I had a fleece rolled, and into the sack, it was time to catch another unless he made an infrequent stop. He could clip with a cigarette in his mouth, but stopped to drink. It was the only time I saw him drink, apart from Christmas and lambing, this time a bottle of beer, mixed in a jug with lemonade.

Small, willing, feet tramped in the fleeces, not strictly necessary or even desirable, but good fun and something I had been doing myself not too long ago. Several small faces peered over the edge of the woolsack at any one time, except when they disappeared into a corner of it and came out half-smothered. So we clipped towards dinner time.

'Bring that little one out,' he said, finishing a monster Half-bred with an udder like the house cow. He gave her an affectionate tap on the rump with his foot as she ran out.

'Grand milker, but not a good one to clip. Dry.'

Most ewes in good condition, and clipped at the right time, had plenty of 'rise' in their fleece, meaning it sat well clear of the skin, giving the clippers a smooth run. A ewe

out of condition could have a dry, sandy fleece, sitting close
to the skin and difficult to clip.

I looked at the little one he meant, an elderly cross-
Cheviot which had sneaked into the flock in a job-lot, and
stayed in by regularly producing twins.

This was more my style. I could carry this one if
necessary. It wasn't. She walked mildly up to, and out of,
the gate. Dad turned her over and sat her up as I started
rolling the loose, monstrous Half-bred fleece in the corner.

'That would make a waistcoat for an elephant,' he said,
looking across.

He had the clippers well set, with a new cutting comb
recently fitted, and the steady zizz of the blades hung in the
air. A bumble bee and a blue bottle made a similar noise
near the roof. A breath of breeze blew in the door. I rolled.
He clipped.

'This is a nice way to finish the morning,' he said.

'She seems quiet,' I replied, fastening the neck wool
round the rolled fleece and pulling it tight.

'She's as quiet a yowe as I've clipped for a while.'

I dropped the fleece into the sack, which was almost full,
and helped the last, and smallest, child out. I had to push
the fleece down one side to get it in.

'Keep this one separate just now,' he said. 'Stick it in the
corner. It can go in the tups' bag.'

The little ewe was now lying on her side. He made his
final strokes.

'Quietest yowe I've ever clipped in fact.'

He cut the last strands with a flourish, and stood up. The
ewe didn't. He pulled the cord to stop the motor for the
clippers, and dug his toe gently into her side.

'Right, old lass, up you get. Grand yowe, that.'

I think he knew then, but wouldn't admit it.

'I think . . .' I started to say.

'Well, don't. She's not.'

He bent down, pulled her head up, then let it go. It hit
the sheet, on concrete floor, with a dull thud. The eyes
stared vacantly. He gave her a vigorous poke with his foot.

Nothing happened. He leaned back heavily against the wall.

'Well, I'll be damned. I've never seen anything like that before. What did you do to her?'

'Me! I didn't do anything. Just got her out of the pen.'

'I've had one start lambing when I was clipping her. And that Oxford tup. But I've never had one dee on me before. I'll be damned.'

He looked as if he might kick the deceased quite hard, but laughed instead.

'I was thinking about the man that had a good old horse. When it died, he wouldn't send it to the kennels. No, no, he said. I'll bury my old friend. So he started digging.'

He finished off what was left of a tumbler of lukewarm shandy, and wiped his lips.

'Digging away for hours. So they left him to it. Went back later to see how he was getting on, and there he was – sitting on the horse's belly and sawing away at a leg for dear life, with two already off at the knee. And shouting, I'll make you fit the hole yet, you old bee, see if I don't.'

He stopped. I looked.

'Just how you can feel one way about an animal one minute, and another way the next. Come on – grab a leg. Let's get the old bitch out of here.'

Autumn

There was something different about September mornings. A crispness, a freshness, a clearness of air that no other month seemed to have. The beginning of a new school year, the end of summer and the beginning of autumn. The end of combining, and the beginning of hard labour.

At first it meant rosehips. A pound of hard-won hips, from the bushes where the dog-roses flushed and flourished in July, was worth threepence. Four pounds of them produced a shilling, ten pounds produced half a crown and a badge, and twenty eight pounds was a whole, green, hessian bagful.

My ambition was always to collect a whole bagful. To try and do that I spent a lot of time scrambling and clambering along hedge backs, and railway bankings. Scratched arms, grazed cheeks and minute thorn fragments in several fingers produced a few pounds of rosehips.

The thorns were the most painful. Like fish hooks, they penetrated the skin much more easily than they pulled out. This was particularly true when a branch, being held down by my foot to make picking easier, slipped out and uppercutted me in the throat.

But I stuck at a job, once started. In and out of ditches, up and down bankings, through and under hedges, sideways, backwards, and upside down, I fought on.

There were better mornings, and better bushes, working in September mist as the sun began to break through. The bushes were small and easy to get at, with fat, round, hips which quickly filled the collecting tin. Poor mornings meant tall bushes with treacherous thorns, giving only long, narrow hips which took half an hour to fill a tin.

Driven home by hunger, the moment of truth came on the kitchen scales. Ten pounds, minimum estimated weight, pushed the needle no further than seven. Another blow, with worse to come at the Monday morning weigh-in when Frankie produced his normal twenty-eight pound bag. Once he produced two full bags and the grinding noise my teeth made drew curious looks from nearby desks.

I didn't complain. It was all his own work. He covered large tracts of countryside by bike on his quest. Also, he was older. And much bigger. All I wanted to do was stagger in, with a full sack, some Monday morning, instead of my usual few measly pounds.

By the time I was old enough, and big enough, to have done that I'd lost the inclination. What was it all in aid of? Was it worth it, for fourpence a pound? What was rosehip syrup used for? The only time we saw it was on a milk pudding dished up by Maude, from the school canteen, as a variation on custard and prunes, apple sponge, rhubarb crumble and tinned fruit with mock cream.

Potato picking was physically harder. But there were no thorns, and it was more like a grown-up job.

We picked them in two ways, either with a gang, or with several Irishmen. Gangs were variable. They were mainly women, trying to earn extra money to keep a family going, and were determined not to be put upon. Most worked hard, if to the clock. A few liked the idea of the extra money, but not the work.

Dad, who found it hard to be anything, but polite, to women suggested to one, consistently holding back the digger by being slow to finish her stretch of drill, that she could go slightly faster.

'The name's Elliot, not effing horse,' she snarled, straightening up and glaring.

'That's got to be a matter of opinion,' he said briskly, and moved on down the drill, tipping the wire baskets full of potatoes into a trailer I was driving.

Jack, driving the digger, had no inhibitions about exchanging views with the gang. His job was to start at the beginning of a drill, and drive steadily down. Revolving feet dug out the potatoes, leaving them lying on the surface. Each picker had a carefully measured stent. That measuring was the responsibility of the gang boss, because any suspicion that one stent was longer than another meant trouble.

As the digger went down the drill, pickers reacted differently. Some bent double and picked as fast as they could, to clear their stent. Then, with time in hand, they could straighten up and manage a few puffs on a cigarette or simply take a breather. Some grunted and groaned before bending down and settling to the job. The idle ones, like horse, took a breather before starting. They were still picking their last potatoes when the digger came round the next time. That was when pleasantries were exchanged with Jack. He grinned at them, and replied in much the same way. It wasn't witty repartee, but it was energetic and convincing.

I didn't learn any new words, but I heard them used in different ways. The pickers also covered aspects of life which didn't normally crop up at our tea table. My grandfather was fond of saying 'To read much, is to learn much,' but I found that keeping quiet, and listening, filled gaps in my education.

If I was lucky, I got a driver's job in the field. Each picker worked with several baskets. Dad and Bill emptied the full ones into a trailer, as I steered the tractor slowly downfield. If Dad wasn't there I got caustic remarks about what it was like to work for a living, or what was I doing that night.

'You never ask me that,' Jack would shout across.

'Not bloody likely – we know what you'd say,' a woman would shout back, laughing as the tractor ticked past. She'd have to wait until he came round the next time for an answer. In a good mood, he could keep a dozen conversations going the length of the drill.

The time to watch them was at the end of the day, as they prepared to quit the field. Common practice was to let each one take 'a boiling' home, two or three pounds of potatoes for themselves. Local gangs stuck to that. On the rare occasions when a town-gang was used, the watch had to be closer.

That year, the potatoes were in the Windmill Field. It was a dry autumn and the gang van sat in a corner. After the mid-day bait, Dad noticed that the van sat lower on its springs. During the afternoon, various pickers made brief visits to it, clutching their coats or jackets tightly. As they clambered into the van at night, he watched with interest, standing, I noticed, between it and the gate.

The old van revved and roared as it tried to leave. It could barely inch forward because it sat so low on its springs, parts of the ancient bodywork seeming to rest on the wheels.

'Bit of trouble there,' Dad said cheerfully, laying his hand on the bonnet. 'We'd better take a look at the back.'

He yanked the back doors open to a chorus of grumbles.

161

'Everybody out,' he said, still cheerful.

With much muttering, they came out. The van body rose slightly on the springs.

'I think we're solving the problem,' Dad called through the open back doors, to the driver who had stayed where he was.

'Why, what have we here,' he said, hauling a bag of potatoes out. 'Grab that, will you.'

He leant in further.

'My, and what's this?'

He pulled another half bag out, then a full bag. He kept pulling them out, like rabbits from a hat, until half a ton or so sat behind the van. The crowd was getting restive as he wiped his hands. The driver had joined them.

'It's only a bloody boiling for the pickers,' he said, aggressively.

'It's only a bloody liberty. Go on, get that van moving. It'll travel a bit better now.'

The van had risen six inches on the springs when it drove away, without trouble. There was a farewell chorus from inside, which didn't sound like 'goodnight.' He grinned as he heard it.

'Short on imagination,' he said, wryly. 'Greed. Plain greed. Let's get them onto the trailer.'

Even a good gang worked to the clock, and stuck rigorously to break times. Irishmen on piece work, being paid so much an acre, were different. They couldn't wait to get started and couldn't bear to stop. The faster one farm could be cleared, the sooner they could move on to the next. Instead of the gang shouting at Jack to slow down with the digger, the group of Irishmen would be urging him to hurry up.

They didn't seem to bend from the waist, but from the ankles, storming along a drill almost parallel to the ground, using their hands like shovels. Everything went into the basket-potatoes, shaws, stones, and soil. Bill and I tried to sift the worst of it as we ran along emptying baskets, because they hated to find there wasn't an empty one to fill.

162

But it wasn't easy.

Dad would calm them down at intervals, demanding less rubbish with the potatoes. For ten minutes, or as long as he was in the field, the potato content would increase. Then they'd gather speed, and more stones and shaws, and off we'd go again. He reckoned that the compensation was the speed of lifting.

If they could, they'd work until dusk. They they went back to the bothy, next to the old byre. It smelled of Lifebuoy soap and tobacco.

There was a general dislike of 'the paddies'. Well meaning people advised Dad: 'Don't be soft with them. They'll take a lend of you.'

Maybe we were lucky. They worked hard, didn't drink much and caused little trouble.

Maybe it was because he treated them with the

consideration he was advised not to use. Maybe we helped. A crowd of chattering youngsters in a small, smoky room seemed to cheer them up while they ate their regular supper of potatoes, bread and butter, and tea.

We found they could read very little, if at all. Tony, the sharpest, laughed it off: 'I'm no scholar, but I know how many beans make five.'

They all did. When it came to haggling a price for lifting potatoes, shawing mangolds or singling turnips, the hard work on one side, and little kindnesses, on Dad's, were forgotten. Business was discussed briskly, sometimes heatedly, but there were no hard feelings once the deal had been made.

The most memorable remark came from Barney, a regular who eventually settled in the area, carrying on with seasonal work, but making a living the rest of the time by digging drains and clearing ditches.

Over the years, he'd negotiated many deals, for himself and his brothers. He pushed his heavy, black bike up the last few yards of hill, leant it against the bothy wall, and removed his cycle clips, releasing several yards of flapping trouser bottoms.

Dad, who knew why he was there, didn't waste any time on preamble. If Barney managed to launch into some roundabout topic, in an effort to wear him down before they got to prices, he knew he'd be there half the evening.

'Hello. Funny, I was just thinking about you. I thought we might manage the singling ourselves this year, because you charge so much.'

Barney lit a cigarette, and pushed a hand through his wavy hair. Business wasn't a matter for jokes. His accent got thicker if he became excited.

'Ah, now, you don't mean that. I made hardly anything at that price last year. Nothing at all.'

Dad rubbed the back of his head.

'What was it? One and three pence a hundred yards?'

Barney's head shot up.

'One and . . . not at all. That was . . . years ago.'

'Oh?' Dad said, innocently, thinking hard. 'Maybe I've got that wrong. One and four was it?'

'Oh, god, no. One and nine we settled on last year, and I was robbing meself. This year I'm looking for . . . for . . .' He thought hard, wondering how far he could push it. 'Two shillings.'

'Cheerio,' Dad said, turning away.

'Wait. Wait. Because it's a regular farm, we could do it for a little bit less. As a favour. For you.'

'How much less?'

'A penny a hundred.'

'Cheerio.'

'Wait. No. I'm robbing meself. One shilling and tenpence ha'penny.'

'I was thinking of one and sixpence. They'll be a lot easier singling this year.'

'One and . . .' He was staggered. 'One and . . .' He ground out his cigarette stub, smoked down to an eighth of an inch in his baked-brown fingers. 'Oh, god, we'll be ruined. We can't live on that. One shilling and tenpence is my last word.'

'I might make it one and seven – for a clean job.'

'Clean job! Haven't we ever not made a clean job . . . one and ninepence ha'penny.'

'Alright. You're a hard man to beat down – one and eight.'

'It can't be done. I've got brothers with families to feed. One and nine a hundred.'

'Right,' Dad said. 'When can you start?'

Barney thoughtfully walked back to his bike and, more thoughtfully, fastened his clips before lighting another cigarette.

'A hard man, that,' he confided to the group of us, watching. 'I didn't get as much for the singling as I expected.'

He straddled the bike, ready to go. His face brightened.

'But then I didn't expect that I would.'

He raised a hand and rode off. leaving behind a smell of

Lifebuoy soap and roll-your-own tobacco.

Plucking

'Go and get another one.'

'Me?'

'Aye, you.'

I looked, dubiously, at the tightly-packed pen of turkeys at the other end of the byre. At my eye level, the average bronze turkey was a big bird by the third week in December, weighing anything from fifteen to twenty-odd pounds.

Bronze turkey production was a long-term process. They arrived as fluffy day-olds in June, when the main aim was to prevent them committing suicide during the first few days. If they could be prevented from drowning, suffocating, or hanging themselves in a convenient piece of netting, the next step was to stop them pecking each other to death. If this was achieved it was possible to look towards Christmas. Us, that was, not the turkeys.

In the harvest aftermath, we sometimes ran them on stubbles which were close to the steading. They picked up fallen grain, weeds and small stones. At night, if they weren't called in early enough, they would roost on anything handy, perching on trees, fences and buildings. When called at the right time, they came swooping across the stubble like small vultures, gobbling to each other as they came. It was one of the few signs of intelligence they ever showed.

Because it was long term, before genetic planning, before relatively easy control of disease, and because bronze turkeys were awkward birds to rear successfully, it was never easy to predict their eventual size. In a good year, if they avoided death and disease, most of them could be in the eighteen to twenty pounds range, with a lot of firm flesh. A bad year might see the original numbers reduced by twenty per cent, and the average bird fifteen pounds of muscle and sinew.

This seemed to have been a good year. It was hard to believe that the fluffy brown chicks, unpacked from a warm layer of shavings in cardboard boxes back in June, had turned into what I saw before me in December.

They were called bronze, but looked black. The red wattles on the jocks, or males, bulged with bad temper. They had long scaly legs with massive feet, which ended in powerful claws. Their fierce, beady eyes didn't blink.

'Go on,' Dad urged, pulling vigorously at the wing feathers of a turkey which had barely stopped twitching.

'Are you sure that one's dead?'

'As dead as it's going to be.'

He paused briefly. Plucking was a job put off until about ninety Christmas dinners were at risk, then tackled in a rush. I could understand that. The sooner it was over, the better I would like it. He slapped the recently deceased bird's chest, where the breastbone stuck out sharply. There wasn't a movement. The angry red wattles were already turning deathly purple. The lids were closed on the fierce eyes. The beak hung open and dribbled a little.

'See? Stone dead. A bit of jerking's only reflex action. Now go and get the next one, save me a job.'

I turned, and looked again. The pen looked no more inviting than it had the first time. I took a half-step forward.

'Which one do you want?' I asked, hopefully, delaying the moment.

'Any one,' he called, from the other side of the bird, where it hung from a piece of rope. 'But get a move on. I'm nearly finished.'

I settled for the decisive, kicking open the doors of the saloon, approach. I threw open the gate and grabbed the legs of the nearest bird. Luckily, I caught both legs. Catching only one, as I discovered later, was asking to be scratched painfully, and usually septically, by the other as the bird fought to get free. As it was, I got both, and tucked my head into my shoulder to avoid the threshing wings.

They drummed round my head as I struggled, backwards, through the gate, shut it, and hauled the bird along the byre. It wasn't far, but seemed further. The previous turkey was bare, except for the black stubs. Dad took it down from the rope, and laid it on a clean bale of straw. I gladly passed him the very live turkey, and stepped back.

He clamped its feet with his left hand, and with his right took a firm grip of the neck, behind the head. He pulled the left hand up slightly, but pulled the right down with much more emphasis. He took the fierce beating of the winds on his chest, well padded by an old jacket and scarf. The neck dislocated quickly, but the beating went on for some time as he hung the bird up by its feet and yanked as many of the big wing, and tail, feathers out as he could while muscles were still twitching.

'Start on those stubs. That's a good lad.'

I started trying to extract the stubs of the thick feathers. They oozed a black, oily jelly as I tried to trap them between thumb and knife blade.

'Why do they call this rough-plucked,' I asked, 'when it isn't?'

'It is the way you're doing it just now.'

'All right,' I said, speeding up. 'But why?'

'They would be rough plucked at one time. I can remember seeing some at Morpeth years ago – just a handful of feathers pulled off the chest. They looked terrible.'

'At least they were rough plucked.'

'Yes, and got a poor price. Who's wanting to pluck a cold turkey?'

'It's bad enough plucking warm ones,' I grumbled.

'Keep going. I need twenty for Alnwick tomorrow.'

'It's not rough plucked, pulling all the stubs out like this. If it was rough plucked there'd be a few feathers left. Or a few stubs. I mean . . .'

'At one time it was rough plucked. Then somebody spent more time, and cleaned them up. Then somebody else took every feather and stub off, and tucked the wings back. Now it means absolutely clean plucked.'

'Well, why, though?'

'Because if they're not like that, nobody'll buy them. Some people even wash the feet.'

He went on steadily, pulling feathers and smoking. Sporadic small feathers sizzled on the glowing cigarette end, making him cough. He looked across when the dead bird I was stubbing squirted goodbye over my hand.

'Aw, look at that,' I moaned, holding it up.

'Run it under the tap. It doesn't hurt,' he said irritably.

'It stinks.'

'Not that much. It'll stop you biting your nails.'

I went back to stubbing, working gingerly round the bulbous parson's nose at the tail.

'And why are they called dressed, when you take the guts out?'

'Dressed for the table, I suppose. Get me another one. A jock.'

I brought the next one along and he plucked while I stubbed, in silence.

The door opened, moving the straw we were using to block off draughts. Several of the others wandered in, bringing with them shafts of cold December night.

'Last turkey for tonight. Singeing time.'

He poured methylated spirits onto a shovel.

'Hold that. Light the match and drop it on when I tell you. Right.'

I dropped the lighted match into the spirit. It flared up in a clear blue flame, a shallow pool of fire with a pungent smell. Dad, holding the dead birds by head and feet, swung them methodically through the flame, singeing off the hair which hid between the feathers and was impossible to pluck out. At intervals, we topped up the spirit.

'Improves the look of them. See?'

The skin did look smoother and cleaner. We ended up with the twenty for Alnwick, our main sale, hanging neatly from the rafters. He stretched his arms, and yawned.

'Not bad. Just these cockerels to do now.'

A Farmer's Boy

'What!'
'Go in, if you like. I'll finish them.'
'It's all right. We'll stay.'

We packed the smaller children off to the house, closed the door and replaced the straw, including a handful in the bolthole. A pleasant fug had built up, with the combined heat of the burnt spirit and the hanging birds. The wind had gone down, and moonlight came faintly through the cobwebbed glass in the corrugated iron roof.

He reached into the wriggling bag, and pulled out a big, white cockerel. It squawked, and fought its head level with its feet to peck his hand. He pulled its neck, more easily than a turkey's, and plucked the main feathers out swiftly, passing it on to us to finish. The feathers were easier to pull, but there seemed to be more of them. We were tired and drowsy, sitting on the bales, nodding towards each other. He drew another from the bag, pulled its neck, and plucked it. Then another. And another.

Cockerels merged into each other. From a distance, he seemed to have reached the last one. The bag lay flat and empty. Two of us were left now, hands hardly moving. Dad held the last bird between his knees, plucking steadily, but more slowly, squinting through the smoke. It seemed a lively corpse.

'Damn the thing,' he muttered, yanking out feathers faster. 'Lie still.'

Another handful of feathers flew, followed by an outraged squawk and frantic kicking. He took another bunch, with the same result.

'I doubt I've made a bad job of your neck,' he said, releasing the grip with his knees, and reaching down to give the bird's neck another stretch. He was too late. With a despairing croak, the half-naked cockerel broke free and ran up the wall.

We woke up, and sat up, as the cockerel set off on a wall of death run round the cobbled byre walls. Dad sat back, hands on his knees. Then he rubbed his eyes, and stood up briskly.

170

'Forgot to pull its neck,' he said. 'Come here, you'll catch cold running about like that.'

He took it, deftly, as it started a second lap, and made no mistake. He pulled the remaining feathers, and hung it up.

'That's it for tonight. No wonder it was squawking.'

I was too tired to agree as we walked towards the light in the kitchen window.

The rush continued up to Christmas Eve. If anything, the final day or two of trying to match available turkeys to the orders he had, affected him more badly than the plucking. It was a question of knowing which customers would compromise, and which wouldn't.

Most of our regular customers would take a chance. A

turkey was a turkey, within a few pounds, and they knew it wasn't easy. Compromise was the best that could be hoped for as he tried to keep everyone happy. Eventually, if we were lucky, we got a Christmas dinner which had very little wrong with it. Possibly a leg missing, a badly scarred back, a missing wing, some small thing like that. We didn't notice in the squabble for the drumstick legs. This year, everyone seemed satisfied with the bird they got.

But on Christmas morning, the phone rang early. Not early for us. We had been out of bed, in force, since five o'clock. The best game, Monopoly that year, was in full use. The five-pound tin of Quality Street chocolates had been plundered. Several squabbles over who had the best presents had started, and finished.

But early for a phone to be ringing on Christmas morning. Dad, who had just put his head round the door of the living room to tell us that all he used to get for Christmas was an orange or an apple, never both, froze. Then he turned and picked up the phone.

'This turkey. I can't get it in the oven.'

Dad thought, as we came to the door and watched.

'Have you got an axe?'

'Yes,' came the voice from the other end, slightly exasperated.

'Then hit the breastbone with that. Hard. Goodbye.'

A few minutes later the phone rang again. Dad, on the point of going round the sheep, sighed and answered it.

'I hit it with the axe. It fits the oven now.'

'Good. Happy Christmas, Doctor.'

'Thank you. And you.'

He put the phone down.

'One more satisfied customer. Thanks to modern methods. Tell your mother our turkey's cooking grand, and I'll be back in an hour or so. Don't make yourselves sick.'

He took a couple of chocolates from the box himself, wrapped the old scarf round his throat, and went out into one more Christmas morning.

Hall

When his motto for the farm might have been 'We never close', it was a mystery to me where Dad found the time, or energy, to start a youth club in the village and raise funds for a new hall. But he did.

He once told a shepherd's supper, tongue in cheek, that he had a great interest in rural depopulation. As most of them knew the size of his family, he brought the house down. But essentially it was true. He was keen to keep youngsters in the countryside, to give them an interest, to encourage them to do something for the area they lived in.

The youth club was a first step, in the old hall we were trying to replace. It was a wooden hut, which has lasted longer than the original builders thought possible, housing Women's Institute and parish council meetings, concerts and jumble sales, dances and whist drives, Christmas parties and flower shows.

I liked it. When younger, we saw it most at Christmas, starting with the carol singing and ending with the party organised by the WI, from 'Good King Wenceslas looked out', through 'The Grand Old Duke of York', to 'The Farmer Wants a Wife'.

The air was thick with the smell of freshly-Brylcreemed hair, soap and coke stove. A mixture of heavy shoes, sandals and sandshoes shuffled and slithered round the floor during the games and dancing.

'The Farmer Wants a Wife' was notable for ruthless energy. In the centre, the farmer chose a wife from the circling dancers. The wife chose a child. The child chose a dog. The dog chose a bone. The bone never really wanted a licking, but that was what it got, the circle collapsing like a rugby scrum, and pounding away unmercifully.

A wise bone crouched down, covering its head. An unpopular bone might get a punch rather than a flat-hand pounding, and start to fight back before adults restored order.

The main event of our Christmas party was the arrival of the Colonel, in wellingtons and Santa Claus outfit, to hand out presents from the tree. Whether the tell tale trace of whisky on Santa's breath was to keep out the cold, or keep up his nerve to face us, was hard to tell.

As I got older, the warm, intimate, cosiness of the old hall was coming to an end.

It was a fire risk with dry rot. More than one energetic dancer on a Friday or Saturday night, had finished a crashing Gay Gordons or Canadian Barn Dance with a foot through the floor. It was funny for everyone else, but also a warning.

Grants for new halls were available, but villages had to show willing by raising several thousand pounds themselves. A local farmer was asked to chair a committee to raise funds. He asked what the legal implications would be if fund raising failed and, instead, debts were incurred. Instead of finding out, they asked Dad, as if raising funds was a speciality of his. Possibly they reasoned that, as a family, we got more from village facilities than most.

He started raising money with the usual hard-core few which come forward from any committee. It wasn't easy and accumulated, frequently by tiny amounts.

Some of the smallest, but most willingly given, amounts came from the youth club where record hops, and dancing classes organised by the older girls, were popular. Bring and buy sales and dances were popular with the adults. One garden fete seemed much like another to me, but the important thing was the money they raised.

More exotic events were held, including the clay pigeon shoot in our Pond End field. In a gathering of fairly keen shots, Tommy Carr, the haulier, who hadn't held a gun in anger, came close to winning. The twelve-bore shotgun seemed to mould into the craggy, thickset figure, eyebrows bristling along the barrel, as he blasted clay discs out of the sky.

And, at almost every event, the spinning wheel of

fortune, made meticulously by Tom Ford, village shop keeper and top dahlia grower, raked in money. Whether tickets were sixpence or two shillings, depending on prizes, there was an unending fascination in the spinning of the perfectly balanced wheel.

The money accumulated, and eventually the hall made the slow journey from site clearance to completion. The old one disappeared, one more chapter in village history.

Towards the end of a mediocre harvest, the new hall was officially opened, a testimonial to hard work and combined effort. A full house sat back to enjoy the opening, and the entertainment.

Dad, having made a hasty change, via a bath, from old shirt and overalls to good suit and brogues, made the introductions, then sat back to relax.

He'd had a trying day, with a broken riddle in the dresser, a stone in the front auger of our 'new' Massey Harris combine, and an outbreak of feather pecking among the turkeys. Washed, combed, tired, but ready to enjoy himself, he saw the new hall fade into half-darkness as a power cut struck.

He sighed, rubbed his chin, had a brief word with the committee, then walked into the September dusk. I wondered if, like Captain Oates, he might be gone some time.

Ten minutes later, we heard the roar of a Fordson engine. From it, parked outside the hall, he rigged up a floodlighting system and the show went on. A little thing like a power cut wasn't going to spoil the opening of the new hall.

Just outside the circle of light I could seen him, standing up, the cuffs of his good suit rolled back, his hair ruffled, dust or grease on his shirt front, keeping a close eye on the temporary lighting. And, at the thought of one more problem overcome, grinning.

One Summer

We never realise that a time has passed away until it is gone. I didn't know it was the last summer of childhood. I was too busy. Besides which, I thought childhood was gone long before then.

There was rabbiting that summer, with nets and sticks, in the pristine daylight of a May morning. There was bird nesting, climbing fir trees and destroying pigeon's eggs. With other birds, we only took one for the collection. This built up impressively, with more than 50 eggs swaddled in cotton wool, in a wooden box. They ranged from the tiny wren's to the large swan's, found addled on the bank of the Tweed. When Donald, aged three, spent a pleasurable hour testing the collection with a toy hammer, only the swan's egg survived. I should have seen the writing on the wall.

We snared trout, lying for hours, with loops of wire, waiting for brown trout to nose into them. Then we yanked the wire, and caught about one in three.

On some summer evenings we swam in the Tweed, fighting clear of the thick green weed, trying to drown each other in races to reach the island, and panicking in case we had succeeded.

I played football fanatically, summer cups, youth league and sunset kickabouts, for as many nights in the week as it was possible to get a game, smelling permanently of embrocation and dreaming of Spurs.

There were cricket matches, open-sea swimming, cycling, rod-fishing, youth club record hops, Helen Shapiro begging not to be treated like a child and Billy Fury finding himself Half Way to Paradise. The Temperance Seven drove me crazy, and I realised there were girls.

As a permanent background, the farm went on, that summer as every summer, from drilling, planting and lambing, through haymaking, singling and harvest.

Most of all there was the relentless routine of regular

jobs. Checking sheep, feeding pigs, moving cattle, feeding hens, collecting eggs, moving pigs, milking the house cow. I helped, not nearly as often as I might have done, and Dad did them all the time. For the first time that I could remember, I wondered if I wanted to be a farmer.

Until then, I'd never had any doubts. For me, it had been settled long ago, reinforced by my first visit to London.

, April in the city had been kind. Park trees were in bud, some in blossom. Our school party walked the street in shirt sleeves as we visited Madame Tussauds, St Paul's, The Tower, went to see What's My Line? recorded, and to watch Brian Rix and Leo Franklyn drop their trousers at the Whitehall theatre.

More interesting still was a bookshop in Tottenham

Court Road, which improved our understanding of human anatomy, and would have improved it further if a flustered teacher hadn't tracked us down, and shooed us out.

We arrived home, after hours of singing and laughing in the warmth of the group, late at night. Less than ten hours later I was hitching discs onto the old Fordson at the top of the North Bank.

The balmy London air had been replaced by a Northumbrian north-easter. It numbed my hands and chafed my face. Theatre seating had been replaced by a bouncing tractor. Dust and diesel fumes had replaced the seductive odour of hot dogs and Kentucky Fried Chicken. The warmth of the group, some of it soft and cuddly, had been replaced by the loneliness of a large, bare field. As I hunched into the donkey jacket, opened the throttle, and set off across the field, there was a long day ahead. But as I opened the throttle another notch, bursting into song to match the engine roar for roar, there was no doubt in my mind where I would rather be.

Now I was having doubts. Not many, but a few. I tried to explain them to Dad on one of the rare evenings I was at home. We had walked down to the Bog, to fill the cattle trough from the ditch, with a bucket. It was one of the jobs I suspected that he kept more difficult than it needed to be because it gave him time on his own, to think.

I was at home because I was, metaphorically, lying low after getting my disappointing O-level results although somehow, considering my crowded months, I had passed enough of them to stay on at school if I wanted to. I had doubts about that as well.

Dad, watching me do some hard work for a change, had no doubts.

'You're going back,' he said. 'And this time I think you should try working. It's grand being able to play football, but there comes a time when you have to take stock.'

I tipped another bucketful into the trough.

'Is that enough?'

The bunch of young Friesians had wandered over, and

were starting to drink.

'A bit more. They're thirsty. Keep going.'

I kept going. There was a certain satisfaction in it, as there is with any physical job where a rhythm develops.

'What about coming back to the farm, then?' I asked. 'If I'm going to do A-levels, I might as well go on to college if I can. Then what? Instead of all that, I could come back to the farm now.'

'No,' he said. 'That wouldn't be a good idea. That'll do.'

I clambered out of the ditch, and we walked slowly back up the Bog. It was the way we'd walked ten years before, on our first day at the farm. We had both travelled a long way since then.

He paused at the gate.

'I don't remember it exactly, but it goes something like – when I was a child, I thought as a child. Now I'm a man, I look through a glass darkly.'

In the late August sunset, I looked at the cattle and thick grass in the Bog. There was a good crop of turnips in the Windmill Field, and thickly-stocked lambs were grazing the Fox Cover. In the distance, over the rising slope of the Pond End, I could see the roofs of the buildings. My favourite ash tree stood clear and proud on the skyline.

He looked at me with that familiar, half rueful, grin. I grinned too. School and A-levels were looming. The last summer of childhood was over.

Also published by Bridge Studios:

A Farmer's Lot . . .
Farmer and journalist Fordyce Maxwell manages to spot the humour in many situations he and his fellow farmers find themselves in and writes about it from his own unique viewpoint. **Paperback £3.95**

Jack in the Pulpit
Humorous tales of rural life from retired country parson Jack Richardson. Appropriately illustrated by Henry Brewis. **Paperback £2.99**

Jack in the Navy
As well as being a country vicar, Jack Richardson also served as a chaplain in the Royal Navy. Hilarious stories of life at sea and in far-flung places are again aptly illustrated by Henry Brewis. **Paperback £3.95**

Jack in the Spirit
Jack Richardson recounts the many and varied ghostly happenings which occurred in the course of his ministry in this, his latest book. Henry Brewis once more provides the amusing drawings. **Paperback £3.95**

The Funny Side of Salmon Fishing
For the first time this book combines risque, side-splitting humour with sound practical advice. Hilariously illustrated by the author, Bill Bewick. **Paperback £4.95**

Cissie
Football's most famous mother, Cissie Charlton tells her story. **Paperback £4.95**

These and other titles are available from:
**Bridge Studios, Kirklands, Scremerston,
Berwick upon Tweed, TD15 2RB.**
Tel: 0289 302658/330274.